That Thin Red Line
Fire: The Case for Self-Defence

Year after year, stunned surprise and wailing headlines greet
the latest set of figures concerning Britain's fire damage. The
beginning of the 1970s brought the crashing of the £100
million annual loss barrier, and each year brings new levels
of devastation. The real cost to the country – estimated to
be three to four times the value of the direct destruction – is
now about £2½ *million a day, or £1400 in the time it takes*
you to read this paragraph. In the light of all the drama of
tragic, much-publicized, awe-inspiring infernos, *That Thin*
Red Line examines in depth what can be done in the first
crucial minutes in the life of every fire. In this age of
do-it-yourself it is all too easily forgotten that while
improved prevention and legislation can do much to defend
us from this ever-growing menace, in the face of the reality
of fire itself what is even more important is the quality of
our own personal reaction.

Stephen Barlay was born (in 1930) and educated in
Budapest, Hungary, and came to Britain just after the 1956
revolution there. His books include: *Sex Slavery, a*
Documentary Report; *Aircrash Detective, the Quest for Air*
Safety; *Fire: An International Report*; and *Double Cross,*
Encounters with Industrial Spies.

That Thin Red Line

Fire: The Case for Self-Defence

Stephen Barlay

Hutchinson Benham, London

For Hedi and Rikki

Hutchinson Benham Ltd
3 Fitzroy Square, London W1

An imprint of the Hutchinson Group

London Melbourne Sydney Auckland
Wellington Johannesburg and agencies
throughout the world

First published 1976
© Stephen Barlay 1976

Set in Monotype Times
Printed in Great Britain by The Anchor Press Ltd
and bound by Wm Brendon & Son Ltd
both of Tiptree, Essex

ISBN 0 09 125710 7 (cased)
ISBN 0 09 125711 5 (paperback)

Contents

List of Illustrations

Foreword
by Sir Frederick Delve

I commend this book to all who genuinely are concerned about fire and its cost to the nation. The author chooses a new and interesting approach to the subject and his work makes fascinating, and in places alarming, reading. His keen perception and analytical mind focus attention upon matters that will surprise readers, and help them understand fire, its devastating effects and the human misery which often follows in its train. The book covers a wide field and its many aspects are meticulously examined. Facts are marshalled and presented in a telling and convincing manner.

It is heartening that an author of outstanding ability should have undertaken such a mammoth task, and should have condensed so much into nine chapters, all of which present their particular story so forcibly.

Having myself served forty years in the Fire Service, for twenty of which I was privileged to command the London Fire Brigade in peace and during the last war, not unnaturally I have for long been very concerned about the appalling fire losses that occur with regular monotony year after year. In the past ten years fire damage losses have risen from £75 million in 1965 to £240 million in 1974. And this is not the complete picture. These are the direct losses, that is the amounts paid out by insurers in settlement of approved claims. In addition to these are the consequential, or indirect, losses. Experts state that the latter are incalculable, nevertheless it is generally accepted that they total four or more times the direct losses.

I have long been of the opinion that there are two certain

ways in which fire damage could substantially be reduced. First is the recognition of the necessity for all industrial, commercial and public buildings – and especially those classified as high fire risks – to have immediately at hand the latest and most efficient means for 'first-aid' firefighting, and for all employees in such premises to be regularly trained in their use.

The second way is by allowing fire brigades to have the opportunity to use their modern appliances and equipment and expertise in firefighting techniques before the extent of fire spread makes this impossible. This is only possible if they receive an early call to a fire. All too frequently the fire brigade is only called when fire has 'broken' from a building and is seen by a passer-by. Usually at this stage the building is already doomed to destruction, and on arrival the brigade is forced to concentrate its efforts on safeguarding adjoining buildings.

In an introduction of this kind it is tempting to comment on each chapter in the book. But space would not permit this and so I must be content to deal with the former point only. This is expanded in Chapter 7 – That Thin Red Line (also the book's title).

Fortunately, very few people in their lifetime are suddenly faced with a fire situation and called upon to deal with it. Most fires are small when they start, and if resolutely tackled with the right type of extinguisher they can usually be extinguished without difficulty. Unfortunately the task of the amateur is made harder by the fact that there are four different categories of fire risk which require different types of extinguishing agents to deal with them. Simplicity in operation and ease of handling are factors vitally important to amateurs. An inexperienced user handling a two-gallon (9·1 l) foam type fire extinguisher in an endeavour to extinguish a flowing petrol fire is a pathetic sight.

Today we have dry powder multipurpose extinguishers which have the great advantage that they can be used with confidence on fires in virtually all risk categories, thereby removing any confusion and uncertainty on the part of the user. Moreover, they are extremely simple to actuate and handle. Elsewhere, and on the Continent of Europe particularly, these and similar types of dry powder extinguishers are in general use. But in the UK, alas, many approving authorities and others still specify types of extinguishers that have remained relatively unchanged over the past fifty years and more. Is it to be wondered, therefore, that fire damage is so high? It is a pity that in this particular field we trail so far behind.

I sincerely hope that all persons having responsibility for legislation on the subject of fire prevention, the local authorities who implement such legislation, and other bodies more directly concerned with the practical aspect of fire damage, for example industry, commerce, insurers and so on, will read and digest the valuable information contained in this book so that in the future greater knowledge of the subject by all will inspire action that will reduce the present appalling high fire losses to the nation's benefit.

SIR FREDERICK DELVE
Director of Nu-Swift International Ltd
and former Chief Officer of the London Fire Brigade

Acknowledgements

This is to express my gratitude towards people and organizations for all the help, guidance, advice and constructive criticism, as well as for all the useful information and their valuable time given to me, most generously, in the course of the lengthy research for and during the writing of this book.

My thanks are due to many officers of the British Standards Institution, the Fire Offices' Committee (FOC), the Fire Protection Association, the Home Office, London Transport, the Ministry of Health and the Trades Union Congress.

I am greatly indebted to numerous people in the British Fire Service, but particularly to Assistant Chief Officer Robert Peskett, Deputy Assistant Chief Officer Mike Doherty, Divisional Officer Frank Rye, Press Officer Gordon White, and Librarian Jim O'Sullivan of the London Fire Brigade; to Charles Aves, father of a Summerland victim, who is so sincerely devoted to the quest for truth; and to G. R. Nice, Head of the Fire Research Station, for the most generous permission for interviews, use of the library and extensive references to the excellent Fire Research Notes produced by Boreham Wood specialists.

A special note of thanks must go to Nu-Swift International Ltd, without whose assistance this book could never have been written; and I am particularly grateful to Find Graucob, Chairman and Joint Managing Director, as well as to several other executives, including Marjory Crowther, Hamish Webster, David Wilkinson and Chris Reynolds for sound advice and time-consuming consultations.

1
Confession of a Victim

'When you discover a fire, you're the loneliest man in the world. You may be a hero or may be a mouse, a genius or a fool, but at that moment you're the loneliest hero or the loneliest mouse, and your life and the lives of others depend on gut-reaction rather than what the old grey matter can work out for you.'

The views of Henry J.W., twenty-two-year-old electrician, were supported only by one authority: first-hand experience.

As he spoke in the sterile air of the specialist burns unit in a London hospital, he was already off the critical list. His bandaged hands and head, with a single slit in the gauze for his right eye, and his muffled, faltering voice, had turned him into a tragically realistic 'invisible man'. Beyond the excruciating physical pain, he suffered as he re-lived those moments of agony day after day, again and again – and blamed himself for the deaths of two women.

But was Henry J.W. right? Was he the real villain of the case and the one who alone should carry the heavy burden of a guilty conscience through life?

Due to shock and serious injuries, he had some blank gaps and murky spots in his memory, yet concerning many of the most crucial details he had virtually total recall:

It was the day when the sales department was to hold its Christmas party, and I cannot say that anybody was much in the mood for work. From the glittering eyes of some giggling girls I knew jolly well that a few bottles must have been passed around during the day, and I knew for a fact that most people's morning coffee had been laced with a drop of brandy or something, but as far as I know, nobody was drunk and as for myself, I only had a pint with the lads. And I felt very sorry for myself because, Christmas or no Christmas, I had to get a few things done right away.

I was working on the fourth floor,* in the new office block where a lot of redecoration and reorganization was going on. It was a huge, open-plan office, and I kept swearing at the painters who left their pots and tins and gear all over the place when I could hardly move around anyway from the stacks of unfiled papers and sheets of plastics and other samples left there by the reps of the company. So it was a right old mess and I very much disliked those flimsy partitions that separated one huge office from the next, but who was I to argue. Except that I was in a filthy mood also because I had a spot of trouble with my soldering iron and it took me ages to get it going.

It just began to warm up when I heard the clattering of the old tea-trolley from below and I knew I'd better go down and get it for myself for she would never come up to the fourth just for the sake of three or four of us working there. 'Tea anybody?' I shouted along the corridor, but there was no answer so I just left it at that. I put down the iron, safe and secure on top of a metal tool box, the hot tip well away from anything dangerous. It was pointless to disconnect it and start fiddling with it all over again – it just couldn't fall from the box and there would be nobody around to kick it. Besides, I'd be away for only a couple of minutes.

Down on the third, there was quite a party atmosphere. Around the tea trolley, half a dozen lovelies were warming up for the evening dance and I had to join in. I mean how could I refuse? Anyway, it couldn't have been more than ten minutes, say fifteen, on the outside. Then I got a kiss from each – my last, I guess, I mean with my looks after this stuff is removed from my face – and then I returned to the fourth.

The smell of smoke was the first to tell me that something was wrong. I hurried up, but didn't run, not with the tea in my hand, and I saw a tiny little fire as I came into that office. I swear it was a tiny one and away, well away from that soldering iron. I swear the iron

---

*Wrong. According to the confidential fire report, he was on the second floor of the office block of the factory. Every other detail about the place in his account is supported by the report, but, oddly enough, his mind seems to refuse the fact that he was on the second and not the fourth floor.

had nothing to do with it. It was on a metal tool box, safe and secure ... No, I didn't look at it, I knew where I had left it and I knew that it would be all right, so I just stared at the flames and decided to sacrifice my tea to put them out ...

Henry J.W. was most adamant about it that the iron could not have started the fire. The fire officer who investigated the case saw two possibilities: (1) that the faulty wiring of the iron started the fire, and (2) that the iron was kicked off the box accidentally. The second version was supported by the fact – acknowledged by Henry J.W. – that the iron had a fifteen-foot lead which might have been buried under some rubbish and rolls of wallpaper on the floor between the iron and the power-point some ten feet away. It is quite feasible that (a) Henry J.W. kicked the lead accidentally when leaving the office or (b) another worker moved it when looking in and calling him to come and get his tea. This second possibility was denied by the two men who worked up there in the morning. Both of them claimed afterwards that they had not returned to that floor after lunch.

Contrary to Henry J.W.'s belief, it seems that only an almost completely deaf, fifty-seven-year-old cleaner was working at the time in a smaller office at the far end of the long corridor. Presumably, she never heard Henry's 'Tea, anybody?'

By the time my brain told my hand to splash the tea on to the fire, I knew it was no good. There was some lagging material on the floor, left there by the plumber who had repositioned some central heating radiators, and that must have led the flames to stacks of paper and a curtain. But I swear it was still a very small fire.

I stood there, staring, for no more than five seconds, I guess. But long, long five seconds those were. I remember every single thought racing through my mind.

What do I do now? Run. No, I must not. If it's found that I started it I'd have to pay. My job at least. It's a good job, pity to lose it. Must put it out ...

I remember quite clearly that I already had my leather jacket halfway off. I meant to cover and beat out the flames with it. But something stopped me. It was brand new. If only I had my old jacket on . . . But I didn't panic. I picked up some plastic sheets and tried to smother the flames. It was no good. As the fire went out in one place, it seemed to come to life at another. I had to get water.

As I ran towards the men's room, I passed the ladies'. Then it didn't even occur to me to go in there. Conditioning, I suppose. One just doesn't think of going in there. I found the tap all right, but there was nothing to carry the water in. I think I shouted 'fire' on my way back, but I sort of half swallowed the word. I wasn't sure if I was meant to shout or not. Perhaps it would cause panic. But must give warning. Yes, I remembered that clearly. I read it somewhere. Some notice or something. No, I'm quite sure that nobody told me what to do. Drill? Oh yes, I see what you mean. Yes, I knew that once a fireman or somebody came to give a talk or something. But we laughed about it and only perhaps half a dozen people went along. Those who weren't too busy at the time.

Anyway, I came out into the corridor and turned to go back to that fire. I must raise the alarm, I kept thinking. But how. I'm quite sure there were no fire alarm points on my way.* I decided to use the telephone. It's only that first I wanted to check that fire again. But I never got back into that office. I was about fifteen feet away when, with a big whoosh, huge flames just rolled out through the open door – no, I had never thought of shutting that door when leaving the room. More piled up rubbish was lit at once, and my escape towards the stairs and lifts was cut off. It didn't worry me because I knew that there was another staircase behind me, at the far end of the corridor.

Perhaps that would have been the end of it all for me, and perhaps those women would be alive today, if I just ran at that moment and if I picked up the first telephone. But it was then that I noticed a fire extinguisher on the wall. That gave me hopes. If I could put out the flames, at least everybody would know that I did my best.

I reckoned it wouldn't take me long to figure out how to use it. I mean the instructions were there, I only had to read them. But there was an awful lot of black smoke and that made it more difficult to read. So I tried to snatch it off the wall, but it wouldn't come. I kept trying. I shook it. At last with a hell of an effort I

*Unfortunately, wrong. It has been established by the investigator that Henry J.W. must have passed at least two 'break glass' type points on his way.

jerked it free. But I had to retreat with it. That smoke, that terrible smoke . . .

And then the blasted thing wouldn't work. I twisted things on it, banged it against the wall, I even kicked it. Nothing. Then I threw it into the approaching flames. I recall it quite clearly: I thought it would explode in the fire and the contents would help to put the flames out.

Then I truly ran. As I turned the corner – there was no more corridor and no door in front of me. Crate upon crate piled up to the ceiling. I tried to move one. I'm not sure if it moved at all. It was very heavy. And I remember seeing it suddenly, that the pile must have been something like twenty feet between me and the door behind it.* I turned and ran into the first office. Yes, I did shut that door behind me. It had a big glass panel in it, I know, because I saw it crack soon.

I wasn't sure if I should get an outside line and dial 999, or perhaps tell the operator first. That must have caused another couple of seconds' delay. I settled for the operator. It rang and rang, and she just wouldn't pick it up. It was at that point that the glass panel cracked. Black smoke had already been seeping through round the edges of the door, but now it began to flood the room. There was still no answer. I suddenly remembered that I ought to do something with the window. Perhaps open it – to let the smoke out. Or keep it shut – not to create a draught.

At last she answered with a hardly suppressed giggle. 'Fire!' I screamed down the line. 'What's that, love?' 'Fire! Fire! There's a fire here,' I kept repeating. 'You joking or something?' I couldn't answer. That hot smoke began to burn holes into my throat.

I remember that I reached the window. And I have a very hazy picture of looking down, seeing people, all staring at me, sort of trying to reach me . . . And then, yes, I wanted to jump, but I knew it was too high up . . . I tried to shout for help . . . and hoped that the girl on the phone had believed me . . .

Later she made a statement to the fire investigators:

I knew Henry well, I mean we fooled about enough, it wouldn't be the first time, see, so I didn't know what to make of it because I mean he could have been making some practical joke and that would

---

*The obstacle was nine and a half feet deep. It had accumulated there – crates, full of old files – in more than a year.

have made me a fool, see, but then he really sounded serious like I said so I thought to myself I'd better be a fool than a stupid ass, so I decided to call the office manager but his line was always busy, you see. Anyway, then I looked out of the window and saw a lot of smoke and knew that Henry wasn't fooling me, he's not the kind, really, so I interrupted the manager and shouted fire and he said I must telephone the fire brigade, but nobody had never told me about that before, honest, I mean not about what to do in a case like that, but perhaps you'd better forget about that because I don't want to get nobody into trouble like . . .

Once the alarm was sounded by the office manager, the evacuation was quite successful even before the arrival of the fire brigade. The old cleaner on the second floor was dead when found by the firemen. Seven people were injured in the rush out of the building, and one of them, a typist about to retire, suffered a fatal heart attack.

Henry J.W. was found in a seemingly hopeless condition. Apart from severe burns, the inhaled poisonous gases caused his lungs to fill with fluids, and only tracheotomy – the immediate surgical opening of his throat – saved him from choking.

His survival amounts to a minor surgical miracle. Scores of skin transplants may eventually improve his appearance, but he lost one eye and the control of many nerves and muscles.

In order to avoid causing him unnecessary embarrassment, his full name has been omitted and the case is not identified. His endless painful self-examination and the merciless pangs of guilt concerning the deaths and casualties are perfectly understandable. But if he is in any way to blame – for senseless delays, the wrong actions and other mistakes all the way – he must remain only the last in a long identity parade of the guilty: the ones who never organized proper fire procedures, who failed to ensure that escape routes were always safe and free, who never taught Henry J.W. and the others how to prevent fires, how to fight them if possible, how to raise the alarm, what to do if cornered, and why to remember the scores of other, seemingly trivial points – like good housekeeping.

For the real tragedy of thousands of cases like this is that with a little training and even elementary foresight this fire would never have got out of hand and would have long been forgotten even by Henry J.W. and the two now dead women.

2
A Case for
Self-Defence

Year after year after year, stunned silence and wailing headlines greet the latest set of figures concerning Britain's fire damage. The beginning of the 1970s brought a tremendous shock – the crashing of the £100 million annual loss barrier. Everybody rushed to analyse and explain away the staggering statistics and, no doubt, the authorities did a good job of it. They emphasized the inflated money values and the natural growth of hazards in our modern industrial society, they put the vast concentration of wealth and risk into correct perspective, they pointed out the increased use of electricity, they showed up the effects of overcrowding, they rightly blamed the social conflicts for the increasing number of maliciously started fires – and they also managed to reduce the shock, remove the sting and make disaster more palatable. So when the figures for 1973 were published, revealing not only an all-time record loss of £179 million but also the supersonically soaring increase of 65 per cent more destruction than in 1972, the papers found only a few lines' space for the report, and the significance of it all seemed to elude the public's attention almost totally.

Once again, it was claimed to be a freak figure due to an exceptionally unfortunate year. Yet the 'freaks' appear to stay with us. In 1974 it took fires only nine months to almost match the destruction achieved in the entire previous 'freak' year,* and the year ended with the stunning total loss of £237 million.

*By the end of September, the 1974 fire loss reached £175·1 million. Admittedly, this included the £36 million loss caused by the Flixborough chemical works holocaust in Lincolnshire.

Losses of such magnitude, and the horrifying message they convey, do not describe even half the risk we have to face. In 1969 Lord Stonham, then Minister of State at the Home Office, warned that the country could not go on virtually ignoring the incineration of the nation's wealth: 'No one knows the total real cost to the country. But if we add on the loss of production, the time men and women are out of work, the cost of hospital treatment, the loss of export orders and of goodwill, the total loss assumes the proportions of an annual national disaster.' For the real cost to the country is estimated to be three to four times the value of the direct destruction – *now about two million and a half a day, or £1400 a minute, going up in smoke.*

It is true that, as with the cost of crime, a certain part of the loss is no more than a forced redistribution of wealth by competitors taking over the markets of a burnt-out company and by builders, manufacturers of machinery and other suppliers obtaining more work. But this helps only the national economy in offsetting the damage to some extent. Individual firms and householders do not benefit from this false ray of hope. For while a break-in or even major robbery has hardly ever ruined a business or a family, fires often have such a permanently crippling effect.

These days, 'no one can afford to have a fire, however well insured a business is', wrote N. C. Strother-Smith, director of the Fire Protection Association in *The Times* of 2 June 1969. He could have added that the same is true about private homes, too, and that the smaller the business, the less it will be able to absorb the losses and the disruption a blaze creates even if it does not leave everything in ashes. Yet he found that 'the outstanding feature of nearly all fires is the total unpreparedness of the firm involved. In the face of the relentless and increasing toll that fire is wresting from the country's economy, it is surprising that neither the Government nor industry as a whole seems to be prepared to take effective steps toward controlling the waste.'

All too many people hope to find refuge in the haven of a

so-called 'carefully chosen' insurance policy . . . even if insurers cannot restore life or heal wounds. In the face of regularly soaring statistics of fire fatalities, several experts were ready to talk about 'levelling off' trends shown by – and found a reason to rejoice over – the 1973 figures: the number of deaths caused by fire was slightly down – 758 as against 775 in 1972.

Yet this bare statement ignored, if not disguised, other data that revealed the *risk* had not been reduced – we were only a little more fortunate and the doctors were a little more successful than in the previous years. For the sad facts were that nearly five thousand people had been injured by fire (two hundred more than in 1972); that the number of malicious alarm calls, keeping firemen unnecessarily busy and away from real emergencies, rose by almost 10 per cent to 62,578; and that fire brigades turned out to more than a half a million fires and other incidents, setting a grim peacetime record. And even this astonishing number of attendances fails to reveal in itself the full acceleration of the risk growth: whereas it took fifteen years from 1952 to double the number of fires in Britain, from 1971 the same proportionate increase took a mere two-year period despite the much higher figures involved.* And the 500,000 turnouts did not include, of course, the unreported fires, the small ones which burnt out themselves or were put out by people on the spot – the ones which are thought to amount to another half a million outbreaks.

Finally, in the basic statistics for any year, another vital aspect often remains unnoticed: for example, in 1973, the *increase* in property damage was the highest (in percentages as well as in actual value) for fifteen years. Kenneth Holland, chief inspector of fire services, said in his annual report published in October 1974: '*This [increase] seems due not so much to a greater number of fires, but to the number which developed into extensive disasters.*' And this is exactly the point which – masterly statistics and other clever juggling acts apart – conveys

---

*In 1952 the brigades attended 85,000 fires – in 1966 they answered 165,000 calls. In 1971 they turned out to almost a quarter of a million fires.

the truly frightening warning of potential disaster round every corner, the recognition of the fact that every devastating inferno begins with a tiny, friendly, pleasing and playfully frolicking flame.

Clearly, the emphasis is on the first few minutes, the most crucial part in the life of every fire. That is when usually the speed and extent of potential spread are determined, that is when the length of the undetected burning period establishes the likely severity of the outbreak, and, most important of them all, that is when the escape chances of all occupants of the affected and even nearby buildings are reduced in geometrical progression by the second. If, for instance, fast-burning foam plastics are present, hot dense smoke and poisonous gases are produced so rapidly that murderously high levels of concentration are reached within one or two minutes of the fire reaching the size at which an alert observer would raise the alarm.* Thus the speedy discovery of the fire and the immediate raising of the alarm, followed by correct action according to pre-arranged procedures, are absolutely essential to save lives and reduce damage.

Yet in this age of do-it-yourself it is all too often forgotten that 'correct action' ought to include more of an effort to put out or try to minimize that fire if possible. In the light of the flaming blunder, which is the story of our losing battle to stop the fire menace, we ought to re-examine completely this forgetfulness and, indeed, question the entire philosophy on which our shaky defences have been built.

Where the risks justify the sometimes staggering costs, our front line of protection can be mechanized entirely. Automatic fire detectors, alarms that are connected directly to the nearest fire brigade, sprinkler installations and other systems go a long way towards better safety for life and property, yet frequently even these malfunction – sending out false alarms, soaking valuable stocks in vain or simply going out of order when most needed – mostly through the failure of the human element

*HM Factory Inspectorate: Technical Data Note 29, 1972.

in their correct, careful and regular testing and maintenance. Where only people, not automatic equipment, are involved in the functions of detection, alarm and initial firefighting, the situation tends to be even more hazardous and desperate.

The various authorities involved tend to blame people – meaning the general public – for the dreadful state of affairs. In common with Percy Bugbee, retired general manager of the American National Fire Protection Association, they name 'men, women and children' as the three main causes of fire. They condemn public ignorance and negligence as the chief culprits – and yet these two remain the most ignored and neglected aspects of the wide fire-protection spectrum.

They improved the fire service with more money, more stations, better equipment and better training – but there was a limit beyond which cost effectiveness would sharply diminish. It is just unfeasible to have a fireman in every house (three shifts, of course) and a brigade in every industrial building, simply because it would cost much more than the current level of losses.

They improved fire legislation to find ways out of *the maze of the 2000 laws*, but, as we shall see, the stumbling block is made of people, as usual, and you can only legislate for minimum requirements rather than maximum protection.

They improved fire-protection propaganda as a major weapon and fought valiant battles against the managements' and unions' shoulder-shrugging instinct, but the statistics still signal 'failure' every time.

Ultimately, the authorities are right, of course, in their con-demnation of the general public attitude to fire. For it is perfectly true that fire is always expected to happen to somebody else's shop, to some competitor's factory, to the neighbour's home – never to us or our premises or the hotel we are staying at, or the hospital where we are treated, or the school our children attend. It is also true that fire is an old, old hazard, we have lived with it and got used to it for thousands of years. Now if you mention a *new* hazard, people pay attention. Flying is still a new hazard – people respect it. Utter the word 'radiation' or 'pollution', two of the newest of the new, and everybody will *demand* protection. Drug manufacturers know perfectly well that all they need to do is print 'new' on any box of medicine to generate sure and speedy public demand for it. In the same way, a new hazard could easily be sold to the public, but fire is too well known to be presented in new, more frightening wrappings, and the boring repetition of blaming public apathy is bound to be equally ineffectual.

Education is, of course, the answer – an answer known to all who care to think about it. Education of adults as a short-term, intermediate measure, and education of children as the only ultimate solution.

The education of the public seems to be concentrated on three main themes.

(1) Basic, sensible *fire precaution*. The half a million fires in 1973 and the still prevailing common practices do not tell us a tale of educational success. Just to mention a few examples: there are still only few people who unplug television sets and even fewer who shut doors in the house for the night; the silent but never listening majority is still ready at any time to keep that British standard fire door open with the aid of a British standard wedge or dustbin, to seek and find 'ingenious' do-it-yourself wiring solutions for any part of the house and overload power sockets by the application of some artistic combination of multiple adaptors, to identify the source of gas leaks with a burning match, to carry that ancient spluttering oil heater round the house and up and down the stairs, and to make sure that the electric heater in the baby's room is well away from the cot and near the window – right under that pretty curtain dancing in the draught.

(2) How to plan and make sure that on discovery of a fire, the *alarm* can and will be raised in some way without any delay so that everybody can leave the danger area immediately, and that the fire brigade will be called. The dismal results can clearly be seen in the ever-growing chronicles of the tragedies of folly.

This author once collected many of the classic examples*
but new ones could be added by virtually any fireman in any
part of the country. Maltings concert hall at Snape, Suffolk, the
then new home of the Aldeburgh Festival, went up in flames on
a clear night at about eleven o'clock when the blaze could be
seen from miles away. Sightseers gathered to stare and take
spectacular photographs. Only about a half an hour later did
anybody think of calling the fire brigade. In Hertfordshire an
old woman was helped by neighbours when her electricity-
saving candle set fire to a curtain. She warned them: 'Don't you
dare call the fire brigade or I'll never speak to you again.' None
of the occupants of this old-age pensioners' housing estate was
thus alerted. The few who noticed the flames and the thick
black smoke also failed to call the firemen. For some thought
that it was shameful to have a fire in the neighbourhood, some
believed that they would have to pay for the turn-out, and the
only old man who decided to take action and walked to the
nearest telephone box, did not know how to use the installation
– so he kept pressing buttons A and B.

Stories of the past? It happened in 1969. Near Manchester,
only in 1974, a fire officer told the author: 'I noticed a flame
in the sky in broad daylight the other day. We simply drove
towards it and found a burning church surrounded by a huge
wailing crowd. Not one of them had called us. Everybody
thought that somebody else had raised the alarm, and several
of them explained defensively that they didn't know the
emergency call was free of charge. None of them was prepared
to take a chance and invest a coin.'

Robert Peskett, Assistant Chief Officer of the London Fire
Brigade, who is now in charge of the Fire Prevention Branch,
has spent twenty-eight years in the service. He will never forget
a nursery fire:

As we went into action, an old woman opened her window facing
the fire and rebuked me most severely for being so late. 'What kept

*S.B.: *Fire*, Hamish Hamilton, London, 1972.

you?' she shouted. I told her we had just received the call. She said: 'Nonsense. That fire was burning for twenty-two minutes. There could have been children in there! Somebody must have called you long ago.' Did she call? No. Had she a telephone? Yes. It stood on her television set. How did she know for sure that the fire had been burning for twenty-two minutes? Easy. She saw the first flames breaking through the roof at exactly the moment she started watching her favourite TV programme.

She didn't even bother to warn the people in the nursery. Although a fire might have been raging in the loft for quite a while without anybody knowing about it in the house itself, the old dear thought that 'they'd surely be the first to know' and besides, they 'might not take it kindly if she interfered' by telling them to run and get out.

(3) The third main theme of education is usually *escape*. Most people are told that they ought to familiarize themselves with alternative routes out of a building and to ignore the lifts in an emergency, yet when there is a fire or a practice alarm they all try to use the route they normally follow – and in high-rise buildings this is invariably the lift. They may know, for instance, that in a fire it is easier to see and breathe near floor level (more air, less heat, less smoke), yet in an emergency they tend to stand up and walk or run – and collapse and die long before the flames will reach them. They might have been told a hundred times that they should shut the front door behind them when they escape from a burning house – yet they leave it wide open, creating perfect conditions for the fire to shoot upstairs and incinerate the rest of the family still in there. And most people must have heard that in, say, a hotel, if the escape routes are cut off by fire, it is best to retreat into a bathroom, shut the doors and windows, seal the gaps with wet towels and wait for rescue – yet, like Henry J.W., they forget about the doors and open the windows 'to get some fresh air in'.

All this is, of course, only an incomplete list to illustrate the problems and shortcomings, but the message is clear: the fire education of adults amounts to failure – apathy prevents the often unimaginatively presented information from sinking in.

And what is even more disastrous is that the future remains equally bleak simply because the key part, the fire education of students, is not taken seriously enough.

Frustrated fire-prevention officers and other specialists and propagandists are full of bitter complaints. 'Human attitudes are the main barriers restricting our chances of success,' said Divisional Officer Frank Rye of the London Fire Brigade. 'Unfortunately, even some of our station officers regard the fire education of school children as "just yet another chore". But their attitude stems from the headmasters regarding their lectures as "just yet another nuisance" which has to be compressed into their tight curriculum for which they may or may not give a bit of time *if* they wish. It's up to them. Nobody else cares. Even though kerb-drills are now accepted as something important for life, and even though they all know that better fire training would pay the country tremendous dividends – although, unfortunately, only in about ten years' time – people don't care to look that far ahead.'

The complaints are just the same concerning further types of education, too. Student nurses and student bus drivers, for instance, are expected to attend a fire lecture or two and to know something about it all, but the examinations never include a single question on this subject – so nobody pays much attention to it. The lack of knowledge about fire will stop nobody passing a test or taking a degree – even if it may kill them.

In view of such general attitudes, the failures of fire education, universal apathy and a marked lack of persuasion and guidance to fight that fire while it is still small and at least seemingly friendly, it is perhaps understandable that our ancient instinct for and old skills of self-defence are diminishing fast. At a time when every motorist carries at least some tools and spares, when more and more people learn karate or judo, when people stock up against food shortages and store emergency lighting and heating equipment, when more doors and windows than ever before are properly bolted, we still rely on others to protect us from fire entirely and lull ourselves into a false sense of security, believing that 'there is nothing like a good old bucket of water while waiting for the arrival of the fire brigade – and the insurance agent'.

That water may not help at all or that in some cases, like electrical, chemical or simple frying-pan fires, water may cause actual damage, has not yet quite penetrated our basic mentality. After all, fire and water are as old opposites as Earth itself whereas we have not yet lived a million days since Christ and the use of electricity is but a moment in the history of mankind.

But if human nature is slow to react to the new set of circumstances, to the new fire hazards of overcrowding, increased use of electricity and chemicals, industrial processes and arson, to the growing risk of concentration of lives, wealth and inflammables, then it must also be recognized that we do not receive much encouragement or inducement for better self-defence from the fire authorities.

And yet more and more fire prevention and other specialists begin to see a strong case for first-aid firefighting, for stamping out that first flame that gives birth to infernos. Unlike the police a few years ago, they do not want untrained people 'to have a go' whatever the circumstances. 'No blind heroes, please!' is the first caution they always give whenever they discuss the subject, but there is no question about it: the presence of an only reasonably trained amateur – equipped with reliable portable extinguishers and/or a good hose reel – at a fire in the early stages can make the difference between disaster and an unmemorable incident. On a national scale, trained early self-defence could rewrite the appalling figures of the annual loss statistics and could help to sort out even the nation's balance of payments problem. But to achieve that, every sacrosanct fundamental tenet of our fire philosophy must be open to questioning.

Legislation has not blocked or even checked the speed with which fire losses mount. With the application of more of the same medicine, is there a danger of legislating community spirit out? Isn't there a case for shared responsibility instead of just leaving it all to the experts, the so-called experts and to the laws, the law-makers and law-enforcers? Isn't there a case for appreciating public initiative and helping people to learn the skills of self-defence instead of condemning their 'foolish' efforts out of hand and teaching them simply to escape and dial 999? Isn't there a case for teaching people, at least some people, to recognize hazards as well as opportunities, for letting people learn that there is a time to run and a time to fight?

Historians found some evidence that the corps of *Vigiles*, the Romans' firefighters, operated in Britain during the occupation. When their organization disappeared from here, together with the legions, firefighting was left to 'well-disposed citizens' who defended the nation from fire, to the best of their ability in a rather disorganized fashion, for some twelve centuries. Their ranks often included the civic dignitaries – a tradition that survived into the twentieth century with even royalty regarding firefighting as an exciting hobby. Organized fire brigades appeared with the Fire Insurance Offices, established after the Great Fire of 1666. Initially, each insurance office had its own brigade to deal only with fires in premises insured by them. But eventually, through amalgamations, bigger, more professional, municipal brigades were formed by the 1820s and 1830s.

Citizens welcomed the change – property owners were no longer required to supply such equipment as leather buckets, ladders, picks, shovels and handsquirts. With that and with increasing need for true professionals most of the public involvement disappeared. Some volunteers, part-timers, auxiliary brigades, and wartime emergency helpers were left as the only reminder that fire used to be everybody's concern and firefighting used to be everybody's duty in the interest of the community.

Today several specialists see a case for returning to a citizens' voluntary fire corps – in a modern form. Assistant Chief Officer Robert Peskett said:

We don't want any foolhardy heroics. But I know that people are only too willing to help, to do anything they can to stop fires, and save lives as well as property. Those who stand and stare without calling us or doing anything are not the only ones to blame. They remain passive because they need leadership. If they had at least some training, and if someone told them what to do – often no more than get out of the professionals' way – they would be ready to do their best. Yet even if they do not tend to regard a fire as something that is none of their business, they are often told just that. I have even heard a good Samaritan being castigated by a magistrate only because the poor man had tried to help an epileptic without achieving much. All right, he didn't know what best to do, he was a bungling amateur, but he caused no damage and at least he did try to help. Frankly, I'd rather have a hundred unnecessary, immediate 999 calls concerning a single fire than none at all or one with much delay.

Bigger factories have, of course, their own private brigades, volunteers led by professionals, and if these are alerted fast enough, they can deal with many small but potentially major fires. They contribute a great deal to the about one fifth of all outbreaks which are extinguished or at least under control by the time the fire brigade arrives. But why couldn't something like that be done purely by volunteers in other premises, too? The presence of a single trained man may make all the difference.

Take, for example, the role of the St John Ambulance Brigade. Their men are recognized easily, they are seen at all big functions, and the public knows that they can give first aid. I'm sure that this often prevents panicky action by others. Members of a national fire corps would be available for just that purpose: to give first aid – an instant combination of leadership and expertise to fight fires in those crucial first couple of minutes between the call to the fire brigade and the arrival of the first appliance.

Mike Doherty, Deputy Assistant Chief Officer, added:

Today there's a Red Cross or St John Ambulance volunteer in virtually every big building. Why couldn't there be a trained volunteer fireman? There is danger, undoubtedly, in involving amateurs, but the hazard is even greater today, when involvement is mostly discouraged, because those so inclined tend to have a go at anything in any case, but now they do it without training and the eye for recognition of serious warning signs. I think it would not be all that difficult to find the volunteers for training as fire wardens – and we wouldn't need all that many of them either – but management in industry, commerce, hospitals, everywhere would need to recognize their effort and make recompense, perhaps by giving them some time off. They don't even realize how considerable the financial returns through increased safety would be. For fire prevention and preparedness for emergencies are negative things: expending time and energy on something that doesn't happen. Our success means that the fire doesn't break out, or if it does it's nipped in the bud, and then there is no proof left to show that otherwise there might have been a disaster. Perhaps after all there wouldn't have been any fire. Fires only happen to other people, in any case.

Statistical evidence seems to support this argument. The one-fifth of fires put out before a brigade's arrival could probably be increased considerably by better first-aid firefighting because now a further 15 per cent are extinguished by firemen using 'small means' and techniques – buckets, fire extinguishers, removal of combustibles, beating out, etc. – which are usually available to people on the spot who could use them at an even earlier, therefore more effective, stage. The result could be that many of these, too, would be extinguished before the professionals appear on the scene – and even that is not all. For the fire brigades put out about yet another 10 per cent of the fires by hose reels, and a few minutes earlier, these, too, might still have been extinguishable by 'small means'. And finally, nobody knows for sure how many of the murderous infernos could thus be restrained in their infancy so that firemen need not risk their lives and resort to their big guns – the major jets and heavy equipment.

If any of these aspects needs proof or dramatic illustration, it should suffice to cast a glance across the Irish Sea, but only as far as the Isle of Man, with its peaceful green pastures, holiday resorts – and the skeleton on the site of the Summerland disaster.

3
Murder – With No Villains

It was the height of the holiday season and the hour when fun was to be had by all age-groups. Would-be dancers and late-night drinkers began to join the players, watchers, listeners and show-fans, and yet the families with children were still around in large numbers – Summerland was built to provide something for everyone on any day no matter what tricks the fickle Atlantic weather chose to conjure up.

The date was 2 August 1973. The time half past seven in the evening.

A young Welsh couple had just arrived with a child who would enjoy the freedom of the no-traffic internal playground and roller skating. The parents could leave him there safely, while they could choose one of several bars, play bingo or watch a show or listen to resident disc jockey Johnny Silver. Two London boys, aged eighteen and seventeen, were busy practising table tennis for a planned tournament against the girls back in the hotel. An old woman went for a walk, ascending all the time through the seven levels of this 'full of holiday magic fun-palace'. Just Good Friends, a pop group, prepared to go on stage: the organist had not yet finished his stint, but the compère had already announced them. It seemed they were to play to a good house – there were already some 3000 people in Summerland. By about nine o'clock there would be 2000 more.

A train driver from Essex left his family – wife, mother-in-law, ten-year-old twins and a third daughter – on the 'sun-deck', under the blazing instant sun-tan lamps, and went for deck-chairs for everybody. Three Liverpool schoolboys were a

C

little bored, wandering outside the Summerland complex. They discovered a storm-damaged, fibreglass kiosk that used to serve as the ticket office of the open-air Mini Golf Course. The locked door was perhaps a challenge. The hut simply had to be explored. With matches in hand. The time was coming up to 19.40. Only seconds later, Miss S. Appleton, at work inside the building, noticed smoke drifting into the Amusement Arcade through an open window.

The fire in the kiosk flared up fast. Flames licked Summerland, but 'luckily' not where the transparent acrylic sheets formed much of the walls. The part near the kiosk seemed much safer than those. 'No risk there,' passers-by thought, 'it must be concrete or something like that.' Visitors were still arriving for an evening out.

At about 19.41 a first-aid firefighting party was already at the kiosk. The technical services manager considered himself to be in charge of the team, but those with him did not know that they were meant to be regular, trained members. They used portable extinguishers, but by then the intensity of the fire was beyond their scope. They tried water, too. A hose reel was passed through a window, but the pressure was low – perhaps the hose was kinked – and by then even their most desperate efforts seemed useless. So they tried to pull the kiosk away from the building.

The moment to fight had come and gone. It was now the time to run – and raise the alarm.

Eventually, a Commission of Inquiry found: 'It may be that a firefighting party, well organized and led and well trained by actual practice with equipment, could have disposed of the preliminary fire before it invaded the building, but we do not put the matter higher than that.' The Commission found that the team fought zealously, but the inherent danger in the situation was that members preoccupied themselves with the flames and – due to the lack of proper staff fire training with pre-planned, well-rehearsed emergency procedures – everybody forgot to call the fire brigade.

The Commission concluded: 'It is necessary, of course, to consider at what stage a reasonably prudent and responsible person would have called on the fire brigade.' The 'building would certainly have been saved' if the brigade was called as soon as the flames on the terrace were seen, but only with the wisdom of hindsight would it be possible to say that was the appropriate time. The time for the call had undoubtedly arrived when it became evident that the kiosk fire could not be fast and fully extinguished. This was reckoned to be one minute after the first ineffectual application of water. 'If the brigade had been summoned then, it is our view that the building might have been saved.' This estimated timing was thought to be right 'whether the properties of the external wall were appreciated or not' by the firefighters. And yet, no matter how ridiculous and tragic this long delay now seems, one must give more consideration to the team's attitude at the time.

The first-aid party was led by a technical man, who, like most people, probably inclined to have some faith in buildings: the fire is outside, and walls resist fire, don't they? And he knew – or thought he knew – what that wall was made of. Immediately afterwards he told the Press: 'The flames were . . . licking the *steel* cladding.' (Emphasis added.)

Unfortunately, he was wrong. The 'steel' was Galbestos, a coated, corrugated steel sheet, with a hidden, sprawling cavity behind it.

For various reasons others, too, failed to raise the alarm for at least twenty-one – possibly twenty-five minutes. Summerland was doomed. It was doomed with gradually increasing certainty for about a decade, from the moment this unique manmade wonderland had been conceived. The first-aid fire party only missed the last opportunity to save it against all odds.

*   *   *

The Isle of Man has been a popular family-holiday resort since Edwardian times. Tourism, in fact, is its major industry. When more and more holidaymakers began to demand 'reliable sunshine', the island government, Douglas Corporation and every hotelier recognized that it was only a matter of time before they lost most of their visitors, mainly to the Mediterranean resorts. Although, by the 1970s, the island had become an off-shore tax haven with different sources of revenue and a new economic structure – once, in a single week, more than 2000 companies paid to register there to exploit tax advantages – in the early 1960s the 'guaranteed holiday-in-the-sun' trend seemed a disastrous prospect.

That was when some original thinking, mostly by local architect J. Philipps Lomas, came to the rescue. 'A scientific and engineering marvel', providing the equivalent of a Cornish holiday village with seaside instant sunbathing, shopping, hillside walks and 'the leisure life of the twenty-first century', with constant all-weather temperature of 70 to 85 degrees Fahrenheit (20° to 30°C) – 'not a building but a weatherproof enveloping structure' – would replace the old-fashioned Derby Castle entertainment centre at the north end of Douglas sea-front.

There would be three major adjoining projects: an Aquadrome with two heated swimming pools, sauna, Turkish and vapour baths (opened in 1969), followed by Summerland, the biggest entertainment centre in Europe, and finally a multi-storey car park (never built).

In order to create the illusion of people enjoying sunshine in the open air, it was essential that the roof and vast wall surfaces should be transparent, glare-free, and tinted to sunny day colours. So virtually from the earliest design and planning stages the use of acrylic 'glazing' was a firm choice for the roof and the south wall.

It was in 1965 that many seeds from which a dangerous jungle of responsibilities was to grow were sown. The site was owned by Douglas Corporation. The project was to be financed by Douglas Corporation and the Isle of Man Government. The firm of J. Philipps Lomas was appointed as principal architects by Douglas Corporation. While Douglas Corporation was choosing and paying as client with one hand, it had the right – subject to local government approval – to sign with its other executive hand the documents to 'suspend, alter or relax the requirements of the building bye-laws or dispense with compliance therewith'.

The clients, particularly 'as guardians of public spending', could have employed a careful selection system to find the best architect for the job. They, however, opted for the 'local boy' – with local knowledge and local contacts and ready access to local officials – to act as design consultant and manage the entire vast project, the spending of some two million pounds, the creation of a 2·5 million cubic feet (70,800 m³) novel monster wonder. The disaster inquiry would eventually find that 'the choice . . . presumably was made without recognizing that he [Lomas] had controlled only a small local architectural office all his life, and that his experience was limited only to modest building designs'. (The firm had only two qualified architects.)

The Principals then appointed, with the client's approval, the fairly young but fast-growing firm of Gillinson, Barnett and Partners of Leeds as Associate Architects. Although some correspondence then tried to clarify the two firms' relationship and the sharing out of responsibilities (Lomas to be responsible to the client and Gillinson to Lomas), a great deal of confusion (or alleged confusion) was to develop. J. Philipps Lomas would claim one day that he acted only as a 'post box or conduit between the Associate Architects and islanders' (denied by those who believed themselves to be subordinate to him), and ultimately, nobody performed the role of project manager. Many important decisions were left to people way down the line of command. And all these were still only a few of the trees and intertwining lianes of the jungle.

There was confusion, plenty of misunderstanding, no clarification of certain planning procedures, and lack of proper communications between clients (Douglas Corporation) and authorities (Douglas Corporation and Local Government Board). So they would claim that some responsibilities were tacitly delegated. They expected decisions and guidance from their architects – decisions that could and should not be taken by even the most experienced and efficient firms. The inquiry would eventually criticize clients and authorities for too much assumed delegation, and the designers for expecting that 'other people should have told them of any mistakes or inadequacy in the plans'. (The Commission argued that designers should not rely on detailed scrutiny and guidance from authorities which do not always have the resources and expertise.) By blaming everybody to some extent, the inquiry was also exonerating everybody to the same extent, though these errors were clearly marked signposts on the road to the biggest peacetime fire disaster in the British Isles since 1929. And the cake of responsibilities was yet to be sliced up into many more portions.

Persistent confusion and misunderstandings might well have prevailed in many respects throughout the designing, planning, building, fitting-out and certification stages, but the architects without any shadow of doubt saw from the start that the envisaged Summerland structure would not satisfy Manx fire regulations then in force. In 1967 their correspondence spelled out the position. 'Some relaxation of the bye-laws will be necessary if they are to get their solarium at all', said one letter.

In another one, J. P. Lomas referred to the regulations which applied to theatres – a perhaps dated law which, nevertheless, could have served with guidance as a prudent starting point. He wrote: 'Since the corporation are their own authority in this matter I would certainly not allow these matters to affect the efficiency of the design in any way.' Attitudes which 'sometimes arose' were reflected by remarks like 'we might get away with it'; treating the Theatre Regulations 'with a pinch of salt'; 'steering the mind of the Chief Fire Officer along the lines of the lowest estimate' in firefighting equipment; and 'I do not think we need worry unduly on this business of fire resistance. The Town Council will have to apply a waiver and I do not think for one moment that they will refuse it.'

Oroglas was the material chosen by the architects for the roof and most of the wall. Eventually, much suspicion was to arise concerning these transparent, moulded sheets, but the inquiry proved that Oroglas started to burn only when most of the building was already ablaze. Although it was certainly not the cause of the disaster, it was definitely a risk to reckon with in the design and building stages. The architects' and authorities' attitudes towards this risk was again rather significant. None of them knew much about the fire-resistant qualities of Oroglas, yet none of them bothered to conduct or commission tests, make far-reaching inquiries or take expert advice. Some of them actually believed (or later claimed to have believed) that Oroglas was non-combustible, despite the fact that its manufacturers had never indicated that.

The Commission bent over backwards not to demand the wisdom of hindsight from anyone, yet it had to state clearly that the risk could and should have been compensated for by additional protective measures like fire barriers or a sprinkler system. The need for such measures might not have been obvious to all but it was certainly visible to those who cared to take a second look and knew what to look for.

Well before the building of Summerland was completed, J. P. Lomas's attractive brainchild was to tempt some authorities on the mainland, too. Virtually the whole of Hunstanton's sea-front entertainment area, an eight-acre site, was to be covered by a huge acrylic dome for some two million pounds. There, however, the Manx architect and his Leeds partners had to face additional problems if planning permission was to be granted. The Norfolk fire authorities demanded, and the Hunstanton local authorities would not dream of disputing, that the extraordinary risk must be obviated by extraordinary fire protection. They wanted a powerful drencher system specifically for the acrylic outer surface (like those installed by American builders with long experience in the usage of Oroglas); they required an above average number of escape facilities; the use of fire-resistant material instead of Oroglas for the construction of the lowest ten feet of the wall most exposed, for instance, to vandalism, and plenty of separation between the dome and any other buildings. These stringent measures meant, of course, considerably increased fire precaution costs, and it was not a mere coincidence that the Hunstanton project was soon abandoned due to lack of funds.

Manx authorities, with a direct financial stake in the project and with the population's interest at heart, could not afford to be too fussy about vaguely rumoured risks. Some dated laws, like the Theatre Regulations, had to be treated 'with a pinch of salt', while others would have to be waived outright. Particularly if the use of certain materials was not only a matter of vital design convenience but of actual savings, too.

This was exactly the case with the entire east face and the eastern end of the south face of the building. Both these areas were originally planned as reinforced concrete. In the interest of cost-cutting, both were redesigned: Galbestos replaced concrete. By whom, how and for what the interior would be used, and what inner lining would face the Galbestos wall, was not considered at the time. (The inner and outer skins were to form the hidden cavity which would, eventually, cradle the initial outbreak of fire.)

The Principal Architect's prediction was perfectly correct: the client and authorities wanted Summerland badly enough as planned – the shackles of crucial bye-laws were removed. This meant that the more expensive and less attractive outer walls and roof with their *superfluous* non-combustible qualities and two hours' fire resistance could conveniently be forgotten.

When the planning application was made, in order to overcome possible objections to waiving the relevant bye-laws, the architect claimed that the building was designed 'to a high standard of fire resistance'. An official brochure, selling wonderland to the public, stated with haughty self-assurance: 'With an entertainments centre of such a size, the question of fireproofing was another major factor. Nothing could be left to chance. The main structure was ideal – solid concrete and non-combustible acrylic sheets' . . . claims that could be regarded as misleading, inaccurate advertising. 'But internal fittings had to

Summerland leisure centre — pride and shame of an island — a mass grave and memento. Metal tables: survivors of the holocaust. The metal skeleton of the fun palace still holds the last of the victims. It began with a single matchstick at the spot marked X. *Keystone Press Agency*

The longest wait — the sickeningly repetitive drama of town life. These survivors were lucky because there were wide ledges to stand on, flames and fumes failed to engulf them completely, the firemen were on the scene without delay, and a window-cleaner, complete with long ladder, happened to be there ready to help. *Daily Express*

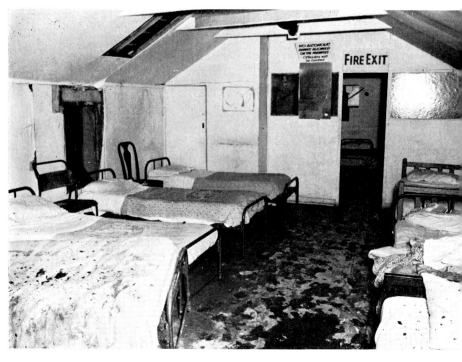

Crowded but cheap — and most guests had a chance to run for dear life when a small fire broke out in this London hostel. Yet there is no sign of attempted self-defence: fire extinguishers remained, and sometimes burned, in their usual position on the wall. *London Fire Brigade*

be of the same kind. Any outbreak of fire in the future had to be one which could be localized to one room or one machine without any risk of spreading.

'Again the problems were overcome . . .'

But were they?

General fire protection for the visitors to the island seemed to be far from perfect. In 1973, only four days before the Summerland disaster, fire chief Cyril Pearson told the *Isle of Man Courier* that the existing fire precautions were 'pitiful', and that he had tried many times but unsuccessfully to persuade authorities to introduce new legislation along the lines of Britain's long-overdue Fire Precautions Act, 1971:

'We are running incredibly serious risks here, and there does not seem to be a lot of action to do anything about it.' The law required that hotels over a certain size should have outside fire escapes, but even this was not fully enforced – few hotels outside Douglas complied with it – and there was no mention of other essential requirements, such as proper alarms, fire-exits, fire-and-smoke-resistant doors or emergency lighting. He added the prophetic sentence: 'It would be bad enough if the present situation was given national publicity as it stands, without being spotlighted by a fatal fire.'

The Local Government Board was clearly offended. The Chief was ordered to appear before it and explain his critical remarks. This meeting, scheduled for Friday, 3 August, never took place. On Thursday, Summerland provided a great deal more than a mere spotlight. A local government spokesman was quick to tell the *Sun* that the building was carefully designed according to regulations. Another spokesman told the *Guardian* that a Fire Precautions Bill, following the UK example, was being drafted. (At the time of this writing, it is still in a draft stage.)

Since the fire, various British fire authorities claimed that such a building would have never got beyond the planning stage in London and elsewhere – unless the special risks were counterbalanced in some other ways – and there were commentators who called the lack of external fire resistance 'scandalous'.

The Commission of Inquiry produced an impressive tight-rope-tiptoeing act when commenting on this point. Determined to be considerate to all and sundry, they gave us an example of how to have it both ways. They acknowledged that if the wall had the two-hour resistance as required, originally, by bye-law 39, the disaster would not have occurred, 'but it does not necessarily follow that the granting of the waiver and the use of Galbestos were wrong decisions'. It was argued by defenders of the waiver that no building was near enough to represent an outside fire risk. The Commission *refused* to accept this reasoning: they formed the opinion that the use of Galbestos in that wall was 'an error of judgement although it would be harsh not to concede that it was an understandable one'. On the other hand – or is this the third or fourth hand? – while nobody can achieve complete external protection or else each building would have to be designed as a fortress, who can afford to disregard the possible acts of stupid behaviour and outright vandalism these days? After all it did not take a bomb, only a lighted match to start this holocaust. So the lack of fire resistance, whether the wall masked a void or not, was 'an unnecessary risk'.

The Fire Chief who was supposed to vet all plans was eventually criticized by some people who saw an ideal scapegoat in him. But his errors of judgement were made in a particularly difficult situation. He worked alone (the new Chief has an assistant to deal with fire prevention), hurried by various organizations, 'steered' by architects, pressed for quick decisions by authorities. Approaching retirement, was he to stand up to the Manx establishment and the mighty business forces and public interests involved in this massive project?

In 1971, for instance, he wrote to the Local Government Board: 'There is a good deal of work still to be done before it can be said that all safety requirements have been met. However, urgent steps are being taken to ensure completion and in order that the opening of the Complex should be legalized, I recommend that the certificate of fitness should be issued now.

'I recommend that this be accompanied by a letter making it clear that its issue is conditional upon all safety requirements being completed without delay.'

The Commission found: 'On 9th July 1971 the Administrator and Secretary (of the Local Government Board) issued a certificate with a covering letter in the terms suggested by the Chief Fire Staff Officer. The Certificate stated, contrary to the facts, that the building, known as Summerland, complied with the [Theatre] Regulations of 1923.' For various, perhaps arguable, reasons, the Chief had not applied the Theatre Regulations at all.

Apparently, some structural and material hazards he failed to appreciate. Although a huge area like Summerland is virtually an invitation to fire to roam freely, and although to introduce compartmentation would not have been practicable (it would have defeated the very concept of an 'indoor seaside village'), similar structures, department stores, for instance, are usually protected by additional internal fire resistance and other measures, such as a mighty detector and sprinkler system which may drench visitors needlessly now and then – not a frequent problem with well-maintained installations – but will spot and deal with outbreaks decisively.

Nobody seemed to have noticed that the manufacturers of Oroglas strongly advocated the protection of exposed edges of the sheets. Yet designers, architects, constructors – and even the Fire Chief and the producers who presumably visited the site of a revolutionary break-through – failed to deal with the problem at all.

The Fire Chief's unenviable position and difficulties were perhaps best revealed by the fact that not all alterations in the building plans were even shown to him, let alone discussed with him. Even some bye-law changes were not sent to him. His advice was not sought concerning the use of Galbestos. Combustible floors were accepted without reference to him.

'By hindsight he wished he had insisted on considerable modifi-cations' in various respects, but at the time he was not sure enough how much power he could wield and on what ground he could withhold a fire certificate.

When the construction of the shell was completed in December 1970 the Leeds firm of Gillinson Barnett took over as Principal Architects to work for Trust Houses Forte Leisure Ltd, who had leased Summerland, undertaking the design and development of the entire interior as a 'leisure centre'. If the huge cake of responsibilities for the varied failures was already ground to fine dust, now it would be atomized so that many more people and organizations could be allocated a tiny share – infini-tesimal but enough to fail a test of blameworthiness.

For if the building was vulnerable with the way the extensive acrylic cladding had been applied, now would be the time to complete the potential fire-trap that could be sprung fortuitously at any moment. For this was the stage when the plans for the inner lining of the Galbestos wall were changed (fibreboard, instead of plasterboard, would be used, adding a great deal of readily combustible fuel), and the ominous concealed void was created. The Commission found that 'such a void is a dangerous fire hazard and a serious breach of good building practice' and that this error 'may well have been the biggest single structural contribution to disaster'.

Those who deal with the fire protection of buildings have been particularly cautious with hidden cavities ever since the Henderson's department store fire in Liverpool in 1960. That fire was thought to have been started by an electrical fault on the third storey of a five-storey building, and although the fire brigade was on the scene within two minutes of being sum-moned, they were unable to reach and rescue ten people trapped on the fourth floor.

Not only was that Liverpool fire a widely publicized all-time warning to architects, builders, management, fire pro-tection specialists and law-makers, but it also supplied a virtual blueprint for the Summerland case.

At Henderson's the fire was discovered only when it had already developed to devastating severity in the *concealed space above a suspended ceiling*. The true ceiling above this void was lined with fibreboard, not all of which was treated with flame-retardant paint. Heat could easily build up inside, leading to a 'flashover'. When the conflagration broke through – in the vicinity of the escalators – nothing could be done about it. The tremendous risk of such constructions was shown by several other fires, too. In a Chicago school the fire spread unseen in a roof cavity and when it blasted its way down, into the class-rooms, it killed ninety-three people. The force of this eruption was such that the pressure waves travelled along a corridor and, reaching the staircase, could still knock down a fireman.

The *Journal of the Fire Protection Association* commented: these fires revealed 'the dangers of cavities created between ceilings and the roof or floor above. In many modern buildings, cavities are incorporated in the design to accommodate services and there is no reason why these service cavities should not continue to be used *provided they are broken up effectively by fire-stops.*' (Emphasis added.)

The Manx Commission found that although not the law, at least good practice would have required fire-stopping within the Summerland wall, and that Trust Houses Forte were entitled to expect sound advice for that from their architects.

It is beyond the scope of this work to discuss all aspects of the Summerland case, but the construction of the shell was not the only factor contributing to the varied potential causes of tragedies. 'The Lessees, as occupiers, seem never to have been aware of how vulnerable Summerland was . . .' and all the work of fitting out the entire complex 'was telescoped into five short months. The motive was the earliest opening date, but the procedures verged on the irresponsible, with too little attention to wise expenditure.'

Beyond the failures in fire protection (structural), crucial shortcomings in fire precautions (including means of escape, alarm, first-aid firefighting, staff training, evacuation practice) increased greatly the hazard every Summerland visitor faced, unknowingly, throughout the brief existence of this 'fun palace'.

*   *   *

The inquiry established that 'No schedule of the means of escape ever existed in respect of Summerland. If such a schedule had been prepared at an early stage in the design it would have focused attention on some of the problems of placing the required staircases and the routes and access to them.' Although, after the completion, the Fire Chief required the construction of an extra stairway, escape routes, on the whole, remained unsuitable. Some so-called *protected* routes proved to be defective, distances along *open* ones were much too excessive. Some were primarily service and access routes, and when they had to be used as means of escape, their narrowness or wrong location created unnecessary hazards, bottlenecks and causes of injuries and deaths.

It is a well-known factor of human behaviour in fire situations to attempt escape instinctively along the route and through the door which has been used on this visit or every day (by employees) for entry. Yet one of the architects was 'horrified' by the initial reports that exits had been 'difficult to find'. He told the *Evening Standard* that perhaps this was 'because people behaved oddly, returning to the entrance they had first used'. If so, odd their behaviour was certainly not.

But another truly unusual pattern was indeed created: in the safety of this indoor village, families tended to break up in pursuit of varied entertainment, and the separation – even between parents and toddlers – might have meant considerable distances both horizontally and vertically. This novel hazard had not been foreseen by anyone. And the desperate search for children and relatives going against the flow of escape was to add to the confusion.

In the hasty fitting-out period, once again, there was not always time – or even any thought – for seeking the Fire

Chief's advice and consent to every detail. A service stairway, 'purported to be a protected emergency escape route', had several doors and not all of these were self-closing or fire-resistant. In addition to this hazard, in order to facilitate the movement of goods in and out of the bar, Summerland staff simply cut a permanent opening with no door in the stairway wall. This was done without Trust Houses Forte permission and without informing the bye-law and fire authorities. Whoever might have known about this doorway later on must have totally overlooked its significance.

(Another bit of haphazard construction occurred just outside the building: it was a kiosk, to serve as a ticket office, for the Mini Golf Course. When many of the bodies would eventually be found inside the building near its burnt site, the Fire Chief, already under pressure and badly shaken, would tell the *Sunday Times*: 'The kiosk was done without my knowledge or any authority from me. That's one thing I'll not be made a bloody scapegoat for.')

No matter how defective and unsuitable escape routes may be, it is essential that the public should easily find them even in moments of panic and confusion. Unfortunately, directional signs 'to fire exit' were lacking and the identification of exits was inadequate. Nobody noticed that in time either.

During the fire some of those who dodged the flames, avoided the fumes, ran the gauntlet of collapsing debris, swam against the tide of frantic searchers, negotiated an open stair-case, and found an exit against the odds, would still have to face the final fence of this obstacle course – locked doors.

It is a totally irrelevant consideration that now it seems most improbable that the locked doors caused any of the deaths. The point is that they were emergency exits and should not have been obstructed or locked in any way (not even with a key kept in a glass box nearby) if anything was ever learned from numerous tragic examples provided by Britain's long, sad record of holocausts. One of those doors which was fitted with push-bar panic bolts had been padlocked. At another exit, milling crowds prevented the opening of the locked door. Even though a member of the staff ran away for keys – and returned with a whole bunch of them to choose from.

How come that not even this obvious hazard had been noted in time? Well, it had been noted. The Fire Service found chained and padlocked doors on pre-disaster visits and complained to the management on two separate occasions. The appropriate fire certificate would be issued only when assurance was given that there would never be a repetition. So the locked and padlocked and obstructed exits were found to be 'a particularly grave disregard of safety precautions'.

A recently retired senior fire-prevention officer of the London Brigade, who now looks after the fire safety of a chain of hotels, told this author: 'We had so much trouble in the past with locked doors that I see no other way these days but prosecution. Under the Fire Precautions Act, 1971, a manager can be fined £400 and even sent to prison for up to two years. The Act, of course, doesn't apply to the Isle of Man. I mention it because we would regard such things as very serious offences. Alterations without proper authorization? Here they would constitute another serious offence with prosecution to follow without fail.'

Frank Rye, Divisional Officer of Pinner, commented: 'Here we take these matters very seriously. If I found locked fire exits in licensed premises, I'd recommend prosecution and withdrawal of the licence. If the building didn't require a licence or certificate, I'd simply have to do what I could to improve the situation by persuasion. If anybody made any structural changes after the issue of a fire certificate, the alterations should automatically invalidate the certificate.'

Unfortunately, once the necessary certificate had been issued to Summerland (relying partly on promises and without a full and careful review of the escape problem), there were no regular inspections which would have been a must only if the Theatre Regulations had been applied requiring the annual renewal of a Theatre Certificate. In these circumstances, not

only the above failures and hazardous practices remained unnoticed. Nobody cared about holding fire drills, preparing
evacuation plans or even arranging the correct procedure of
raising the alarm and calling the fire brigade. Some executives
were quick to point out that this was the busy height of the
season and that the rapid turnover of staff made fire training
particularly difficult to organize. This, indeed, is a serious
problem for all hotels and places of entertainment at every
seasonal holiday resort, but when management takes some
interest and supervision rises above the irresponsibly lacka-
daisical, fire precautions cease to set superhuman tasks.

Trust Houses had 'an excellent document' for the guidance
of General Managers 'in safeguarding the public and property
under their control'. Unfortunately, the last General Manager of
Summerland never saw this document. It might have been among
the files handed over to him by his predecessor, but he never
read it. Confusion existed not only within the Summerland
management, but also up to Trust Houses Forte Leisure Ltd
head office, concerning the allocation of various duties. The
group's Deputy Managing Director's views conflicted with those
held by his Group Fire and Safety Officer; the General Manager
of Summerland hoped for staff initiative and relied on heads
of department without ever instructing them in what was
expected of them. 'In this thoroughly unsatisfactory state of
affairs it is not surprising that the fire found the entire staff
completely unprepared and at a loss.' But if people were allowed
to *assume* too much at every level of the chain of command, it
was ultimately the responsibility of the higher authority (the
group) to ensure that managers and executives were aware of
their duties and supervise the satisfactory performance of all
delegated powers.

And finally there was an elaborate alarm system, combined
with means of immediate public announcements on all loud-
speakers, but nobody had been given the *personal* responsibility
to sound the alarm or warn the public or, indeed, order the
evacuation, because apparently it was generally assumed that

D

somebody would surely do all these things, including the use of one of the numerous 'break glass' alarm points.

Once again there is an uncanny resemblance to the Liverpool department store situation. At Henderson's the self-closing doors had been wedged open on each floor – with that the enclosed stairways ceased to be protected. There were open escalators. There were customers and outside contractors' workmen – all strangers – all over the building. Automatic detection and alarm installation was already planned, but at the time only a manual alarm system could be operated by bells on each floor. The existing system was completely satisfactory . . . as long as somebody was prepared to use it without delay.

Two workmen, laying linoleum near the goods lift, noticed a shower of sparks dropping down the shaft. One of them went up to the third floor to find out what was happening, and then up to the fourth storey for some extinguishers. He tried to fight the fire – in vain. Store employees, also unaware of the raging fire in the concealed cavity, tried to deal with minor outbreaks and attempted to salvage stock. They did not sound the alarm.

Meanwhile, at about 14.20, the store manager was on the third floor. His attention was attracted by a crackling noise above the ceiling. He then saw a brilliant flickering through some gaps. He telephoned the switchboard and told the operator to call the fire brigade. The brigade received the call at 14.23. In those crucial lost moments there was no sign of smoke or fire on the fourth floor – where eventually the victims would be trapped. The manager was using a water extinguisher, directing the jet upwards. The water, of course, just bounced off the ceiling tiles. The operator then rang back to ask the manager if the alarm to evacuate should be sounded. He instructed her to sound the alarm and went to meet the brigade at the door. Some of the gallant staff continued the attempt to save lives, stock and the building, while business was 'as usual' on the ground floor – until the brigade ordered everybody to leave.

The Liverpool inquest found that if the staff had received 'timely and efficient instruction in fire emergency', an immediate sounding of the alarm and organized evacuation might well have saved at least some lives. This store disaster had a direct bearing on the birth of the Offices, Shops and Railway Premises Act – in 1963.

Almost precisely ten years later, in the Isle of Man, the writing was clearly on the wall, but those who were supposed to read it proved themselves shortsighted or illiterate.

On the evening of 2 August 1973 the Summerland scene was set for disaster. The brave but untrained and unprepared first-aid firefighting party was already in action at the burning kiosk, the fire was already turning the wall cavity into a fierce furnace, but for most people it was still only an evening of routine: work for some and fun for most.

Although smoke had been seen outside at 19.40 and fire-fighting at the kiosk had begun at about 19.41, visitors were still arriving and paying to enter the building almost twenty minutes later. At about the same time, some smoke seeped through the wall – the void could not contain the fire much longer. But the boys were still busy with their table-tennis practice, the Essex train driver was still anxious to obtain deck-chairs for all the family, the Welsh couple settled for the show-bar, leaving their child free to skate, and the three Liverpool boys were seen running from the scene of their childish prank.

At about 19.58 some people decided to leave because of the smoke. But they were told it was only a chip-pan fire, so they stayed on. The organist, about to finish his shift, was asked to play on for a few minutes to prevent panic. 'I'll play the "Blue Danube" to put out that tiny fire,' he reassured his audience. The development of the holocaust was well under way – flaming vapours erupted from the wall and 'fire massively invaded the Amusement Arcade' – but the alarm to evacuate and summon the fire brigade was still not sounded. The time was just after eight o'clock.

The fire brigade received, however, two calls in quick succession: one came from a taxi driver who sent a message by radio via his head office – the other came from a ship at sea. A 'first attendance' force of three engines was on its way without delay. The firemen were already at the scene – and asked for the island's entire brigade of sixteen engines and 106 men, mostly part-timers, to come as reinforcements – when at last the direct Summerland alarm sounded at the fire station at 20.05. By that time it was pandemonium in fun palace. A 'rolling waterfall' of flames was seen engulfing the Amusement Arcade, tackling the wall, sweeping along the ceiling, climbing up and over the edge of the second terrace above. People began to run. Screams began to fill the huge hall. And there was still no evacuation alarm or central announcement. Only the General Manager, racing the crowd to break open locked emergency doors, shouted his evacuation instruction to the organist, who, in turn, stopped playing and yelled 'Everybody out!'

Whatever happened to the elaborate alarm and public announcement system? Problem No. 1 concerning this equipment was the lack of any attempt to make use of it. The staff had not been properly instructed and trained. When the Technical Services Manager realized that he was losing the battle against the kiosk fire – at about one minute past eight! – he asked the House Manager to call the brigade. The House Manager then overlooked the existence of the automatic alarm system, rushed to a public telephone box, and made the call from there.

When at last the system was used, at 20.05, it failed to sound its automatic sirens and bells for evacuation inside the building – probably because the fire had already attacked and short-circuited the wiring – which might be just as well, for the sirens, without explanation and guidance to the exits, could have increased the panic even more. For the nerve centre of the building, from where the 'what-to-do' should have come, was manned by a girl who could only run for it when the moment came. She had not been prepared for emergencies. There was a small fire notice in the control room, but she never read it. Her job was to control some sound and lighting equipment, make public announcements about entertainment, and play recorded music. She had telephone contact with all and a commanding view of most parts of the building, but she had no idea that she was meant to keep an eye on trouble, spot fires, press the alarm button, and activate a switch to make her own voice heard on every loudspeaker over any other microphone users at the time. In the circumstances, running for dear life was the only prudent course of action left to her.

Undoubtedly, many of the staff put up a heroic fight and some of them gave their lives to save members of the public in their care. But they acted in an unprepared, haphazard fashion, making 'errors of judgement, errors of action and errors of inaction. They were all human errors and failings and are not to be derided by us who were not involved at the time,' declared the inquiry which blamed lack of training for their mistakes. One of the more serious of such errors was made by the House Manager who 'turned off the main electricity supply, thinking that this was the right thing to do and being ignorant of the written instruction to the contrary'. This happened at 20.11, when the building was ablaze everywhere, when escapers needed every help they could get, and when the exits and stairways, already enveloped in lethal fumes, were now suddenly plunged into total darkness – for the system that should have activated stand-by emergency lighting also failed.

There were about 3000 people in Summerland at the time. It was a miracle that only fifty were killed. A couple of hours later there would have been 5000 people in there, and the loss of lives, with the accumulation of panic and stampede, could have increased to hundreds. Because the scene was set for all the errors and shortcomings of planning, building, checking, certifying, fire precautions and fire prevention, all the factors of doom, to manifest themselves with disastrous effects. The fully developed fire broke out of the wall. The Oroglas was attacked. The gap between the wall and the terrace edges created a 'chimney' that killed people on the stairs there as if a flamethrower squad had been thrown in.

Separated families fought to go against the stream of escape to find loved ones. At locked doors, as well as along too-narrow escape routes, frightful bottlenecks developed. Not only children but also strong grown-ups fell to be trampled on by the panic-stricken crowd. Some people jumped from the terraces. Parents, stuck in the jam on the stairs, dropped their children to the floor below – hoping for the best. Many of them were caught by members of the staff. Others were lucky to land on top of people rather than rigid objects.

Shocked survivors claimed that the spread of the fire was incredibly rapid: 'It was suddenly everywhere in less than ten minutes.' They had seen only the last ten of some thirty-five minutes.

That Welsh couple was miraculously reunited with their child who was still on roller skates. But the Essex train driver lost his entire family, all five of them. And the boys were never to play in the hotel tournament against the girls.

Soon the firemen's 'stop' message indicated that the fire was 'under control', but in lay terms it meant that it was all over, fifty men, women and children, and 'holiday wonderland' were no more. The time was 21.10. With another thirty minutes of safety to go if only that outside wall, next to the kiosk, had the usual two-hour fire resistance.

*   *   *

A month after the fire, on 3 September 1973, the Lieutenant-Governor of the Isle of Man appointed the Summerland Fire Commission by Warrant, under the chairmanship of the Hon. Mr Justice Cantley, O.B.E. The other two members were, by invitation from England, Professor Denis Harper of Manchester University's Building Department, and P. S. Wilson-Dickson, O.B.E., a senior civil servant from the Home Office Fire Inspectorate. After a lengthy public hearing, several inspections of the Summerland site, scrutiny of all the evidence and submissions by interested parties, and consultations with a great variety of experts, the Commission produced a most impressive 40,000-word report which was published in May 1974.

Although the report took a considerate and well-balanced view of the numerous factors that potentially contributed to the disaster, and although a senior Manx civil servant called it 'gentle in its condemnation and generous in its praise',* it did not shirk from naming names, spotlighting weaknesses and pointing an accusing finger at the origins of mistakes and unpreparedness. At the end, the report made thirty-four most valuable recommendations, but before that, its far-reaching conclusions were summed-up in paragraph 246:

> In all the above inadequacies and failings, it seems to the Commission that there were no villains. With a certain climate of euphoria at the development of this interesting concept, there were many human errors and failures and it was the accumulation of these, too much reliance upon an 'old boy' network and some very ill-defined and poor communications which led to the disaster. It would be unjust not to acknowledge that not every failure which is obvious now would be obvious before the disaster put structure and people to the test.

There were no villains. Perhaps in a strictly legal sense this is correct. The Manx laws, as they were, might not have been broken – when they were too much of a nuisance, they were simply altered by those who were entitled to do so. So perhaps it is true, perhaps there were no villains. It is perhaps not villainous to forgo certain responsibilities, to settle for subnormal standards, to omit making research or seeking expert advice, to relinquish duties of supervision, to tolerate obvious failures (if not *all* were obvious before the disaster, *some* must have been), to 'assume' too much instead of checking, and to build and manage in a manner that raises issues of 'great concern to the architectural profession'.†

Perhaps one could argue that the much-criticized, now retired, Chief Officer of the Manx Fire Service was wrong in saying: 'No villains? That is not my opinion, but I don't think

Daily Telegraph, 24 May 1974.
†Royal Institute of British Architects quoted by *Building*, May 1974.

I can say any more. I don't want to leave the island with an atmosphere of being against the Government.'*

Perhaps one could dispute, in some ways, the view expressed by Tyrone Bird, technical editor of *Construction News*: 'The conclusion that there were "no villains" was a serious error of judgement. . . . The report presented a clear picture of incompetence and irresponsibility far beyond the bounds of professional good practice.'

And perhaps one could discount all the rumours about the existence of a 'Manx Mafia', corruption and other sinister aspects of the functions of an 'old-boy network'.

But all this is only a secondary consideration. The primary question is: had the Commission any authority to apportion blame, pass judgement and, by the same token, exonerate to the extent of the 'no villains' statement?

The terms of reference which apply to British public inquiries vary with the legislation under which the commissions are appointed. A full public inquiry is always authorized by a minister, who then informs Parliament about his decision. If it is an inquiry concerning a fire disaster, the minister responsible for it may make the decision and the announcement together with the Home Secretary.

If an aviation accident investigation culminates in the classic court drama of a public inquiry its sole aim is the finding of the truth. When the cause of an accident is eventually expounded in the report, 'truth' may mean an open or implied assignment of responsibility to some people, equipment or facility. But these reports always speak about the 'probable cause'. The inquiries are certainly not authorized to blame or exonerate any party, and they are not meant to be used as a basis for criminal or civil proceedings, insurance claims or disciplinary actions. Subsequent litigation may, in fact, contradict the report, although this is an obviously difficult task, for it may require the services of as outstanding experts as those who investigate the case and assist the public inquiry which, in itself, is entirely in

*Dail Mail, 25 May 1974.

the hands of laymen – who happen to be lawyers because they know how to conduct fact-finding exercises like these.

When a case of national importance concerns, for example, the health and social services, the minister may order a public inquiry which is, once again, to establish facts, discover the truth, make recommendations and so help to avoid recurrence. It is inevitable that some praise and criticism should be directed, even through the plainest statement of facts, towards certain individuals or organizations. But in accordance with the terms of the Commission's appointment it is not for these public inquiries to apportion blame, pass judgement, exonerate, let alone mete out punishment.

Some exceptions do occur and these ought to receive more attention than at present customary. For example, after the deaths of twenty-four patients in a Shrewsbury mental hospital a Committe of Inquiry was appointed 'on April 19th 1968 under Section 70 of the National Health Services Act, 1946' with the 'terms of reference being to *inquire into the circumstances* leading to a fire at Shelton Hospital . . . and to report thereon.' (Author's italics.) This Committee, nevertheless, not only distributed criticism quite freely, but – in its zealous effort to condemn serious failures like the lack of evacuation drill and staff fire training – it also chose to state that 'a number of persons in responsible positions from the Shrewsbury Hospital Management Committee downward contributed towards 'those failures and merit varying degrees of blame'.

Marine inquiries are more to the point. Under the Merchant Shipping Act of 1894, a Preliminary Inquiry may be held in cases of certain irregularities, casualty at sea, etc. This is a fact-finding inquiry, conducted privately, where parties concerned cannot make representations and thus cannot be blamed or accused. If there it emerges that further investigation is necessary and charges may be preferred, a Formal Inquiry can be held. This is then a public inquiry, where all parties must be heard or properly represented, because at the end, people and their conduct may be blamed and action against them –

including the withdrawal of a Master's Certificate – can be recommended. The terms of reference do not spell out these rights. They speak about an 'inquiry into the circumstances' of a case and about the right to make orders concerning costs, but the 1894 Act itself empowers the Formal Inquiry to apportion blame.

In the Summerland case, no specific statutory authority concerning the appointment of the Commission was invoked. The Lieutenant-Governor of the island has the right, *ex officio*, to order an inquiry and define its terms of reference. Thus he instructed the Commission 'to inquire into, and report on, all the circumstances of, and leading up to, the fire ... and to make recommendations' – not to determine if there were or were not any villains.

The Commission needed the backing of only one additional piece of legislation. Therefore, under the Inquiries (Evidence) Act, 1950, Tynwald authorized the Commission to summon witnesses and take evidence on oath. Like the terms of reference, this Act gives no right to pass judgement. Although reluctant witnesses can be accused of contempt of the Commission, the charge must be dealt with by the High Court and not the Commission itself. The Act authorizes the Commission to make orders as to the costs of the inquiry. And that is all. So was it right and proper for the Commission to state its view of ultimate exoneration so clearly?

Had there been any final condemnation of certain people or organizations, they would have argued most forcefully that the Commission went beyond its terms of reference. The Isle of Man Government would have been entitled to disregard the findings. In the actual circumstances, however, a great deal of use was made of the Report.

At the inquest in August 1974 it was announced that the Attorney General for the Isle of Man was not contemplating criminal proceedings against anyone in respect of the disaster. Calling only two witnesses, the coroner told the jury that he had read the Report again and again and found that the evidence did not amount to criminal negligence against anyone. He specifically drew the jury's attention to the fact that the Report had found errors and failures, but no villains. He emphasized that the matter was very involved and that the jury was fortunate in having the independent Report, and three eminent experts' conclusions to assist them in judging the issues. He explained that this was not a case of a single act of negligence or one fatal omission. The responsibilities were divided among many parties.

At noon the inquest was adjourned for two hours. As the jury were filing out of the court room, each member was handed a copy of the long and complicated Report. It was, indeed, understandable that the coroner had to read it 'again and again' to do justice to it. It was even more understandable that the jury were out for three hours instead of two, scrutinizing the facts and arguments, set out at half the length of a novel. And it would seem a safe bet to assume that probably the jury read mostly the 'conclusions' – with Paragraph 246 making the final impression.

As directed by the coroner, the jury returned a unanimous verdict of deaths by 'misadventure'.

Some of the victims' relatives feel that the entire inquiry was part of a whitewashing job, and that the inquest was farcical. They and their MPs are still pressing for more satisfactory answers, explanations and admissions of acts of villainy. Meanwhile, many of the 1600 hotels and boarding houses of the Isle of Man continue to represent a serious fire hazard, described by the former Fire Chief as scandalous.

*   *   *

The three Liverpool boys – aged fourteen, twelve and twelve – were caught. They admitted that they ignited the kiosk with matches. They did not intend to start a major fire. For causing wilful and unlawful damage to the kiosk lock, Douglas Juvenile Court fined the only villains £3 each, and ordered each to pay 33p compensation and 15p costs.

4
The Fire Risk
We Live With

We like to believe, because it gives us instant reassurance, that it always happens to somebody else. Only somebody else's premises will burn, as if ours were non-combustible. It is equally easy to dismiss the risk Summerland was exposed to – it was the victim of sheer, thoughtless vandalism, after all. But if those boys were innocent in a certain sense because they had never worked out the consequences of their irresponsible pastime, none of those connected with the planning, building, running or supervising of Summerland could disclaim responsibility on a similar basis because it was up to them to work out the risks, evaluate the hazards – including vandalism – and provide reasonable protection against all.

This is probably one of the most crucial factors of the unstoppable soaring of fire losses: the fire risk is often allowed to remain 'unknown'; it may not be fully understood (or only misunderstood); and sometimes it is not studied at all or even thought about.

The evaluation of risk, because of its complexity, ought to be treated as a task for a specialist with every responsible person related to the project taking a keen interest. It is, however, frequently left to 'the office boy' (as a leading fire insurer put it) or, according to a fire-prevention specialist, it is the responsibility of an expert fire officer, though he is regarded as just 'an unproductive employee, a pain in the neck, who is given no authority to make decisions, no power to get decisions made, and no standing to back his own recommendations'. It is almost proverbial that fire officers tend to be the most frustrated men in any organization and if their efforts become too much of a nuisance they are threatened that they will be – and often are – replaced by a storeman or anybody 'who can spare the time'.

New legislation can enforce certain preventive measures, but the law itself cannot educate management and change attitudes. Fire authorities still expect that they will have to continue using the technique nicknamed 'The Bluff and Persuasion Act, XXth century' and that managing directors even of smaller firms will tend to remain unavailable for discussions on fire matters. It is a sad summary of the general apathy that the fire education and guidance of numerous big and small businesses is performed solely by fire-equipment manufacturers' often well trained but not entirely unbiassed representatives. These men find that the buying of, say, an alarm system may be done 'by whoever happens to be free at the time'. It is perhaps understandable that buyers keep asking these reps for 'something cheaper' than the equipment most recommended because the seller's bias and interest are obvious. It shows, however, the lack of faith in company fire officers that their choice and recommendations are also judged only by the price-tag.

Unfortunately, risk evaluation may be left to fate – and fire obliges the fatalist all too frequently. For example, Find Graucob, Chairman of a leading international fire-equipment manufacturer, showed this author a brewery's order for 150 dry-powder extinguishers. It was marked 'urgent' and a note in the space left for delivery instructions said: 'TO BE COLLECTED – IMMEDIATELY'. The story behind it was, of course, that representatives had tried for months and months in vain to make a sale but only a devastating blaze could win the management's attention. On the night when the fire broke out, several workers ran all over the place in search of an extinguisher in working order. The few aged, old-fashioned containers they found failed to operate. The direct damage exceeded £2 million without counting the value of lost production and sales. Early in the morning, while the fire brigade was still busy at the scene, the brewery sent a lorry to pick up as many of the 150

extinguishers as could be found in the manufacturer's warehouses, so that the buildings that had not been gutted could be
re-equipped without any delay. (Unlike the old Factories Act,
the Fire Precautions Act also specifies the maintenance of
equipment.)

Managers of many big and small companies fail to appreciate
the disastrous importance of a fire because they believe that the
insurers will cover them in full. Yet occasionally, the odd half-
sentence can convey the true message and demonstrate how
highly fires and their effects should really be ranked.

In September 1974 Ferranti's, the mammoth, privately
owned defence and electronics firm, revealed a major financial
crisis. Although the group had sixteen factories in Britain,
employing some 16,000 people, its main bankers refused to
increase any further the already huge overdraft of some £20
million, and government aid had to be sought. For the group's
poor performance in the year to March 1974 chairman Sebastian
de Ferranti blamed the three-day week, serious industrial disputes at home and abroad, two major fires at two key plants,
and government price controls. Fires have probably never been
listed in more prominent company of doom.

Modern management studies strongly focus on training
would-be executives for positive thinking. While consolidating
positions is a vital part of sensible and well-planned progress,
investments and risks are examined in the light of projected
additional profits and expansion. In this sense the 'mere protection' of life and property in their care may appear to many
as negative outlook. No sprinkler system increases production,
alarms and detectors do not improve efficiency, extinguishers
do not boost sales, and fire drills and means of escape will
hardly brighten the company's international image. Yet the lack
of these will achieve the opposite results without fail. Production
and efficiency will be reduced, sales will diminish, and – through
the unnecessary loss of lives – the company image will lose its
sparkle in the wake of a major fire. (It is often thought that
'major' fires can occur only at the major establishments of

major companies. This is, of course, an entirely false point of view. The burning of one child and the gutting of a mere fish-shop are as major fires affecting a family or an owner as those that hit Ferranti's.) Hence the foresight, bold planning and un-compromising execution of those plans are the factors that create the elements of a truly *positive* approach to fire prevention by dashing modern management.

Further differences between approaches can be measured by the management's attitude to the law. It is a sign of negative thinking to care only about the immediate profits, not to make allowances for safeguarding all the profitable activities, and to 'economize' by insisting on the minimum one can legally get away with. A positive yet irrational approach may be just as damaging to a business: it is no good investing £10 in equipment to protect assets of £1, and experts/salesmen only damage a good cause by advocating senseless extravagance.

The cost effectiveness of fire prevention must be a corner-stone of positive managerial thinking. Although sprinklers, for instance, qualify for tax relief and insurance premium reduction, the cost of installation and careful maintenance (or else of damage by accidental discharge) are still so high that the introduction of the system is justified only in the most exposed and most valuable areas, such as capital intensive process industries that work with highly flammable materials, depart-ment stores or high-stacked storage facilities.

The risks and the justifiable cost of protection are bound to look different to managers, financial and production execu-tives, protection specialists, fire authorities, local authorities, insurers and equipment manufacturers. Although the Fire Protection Association has produced some valuable checklists in general terms which are a good starting point for laymen, there is no perfect, all-purpose guide-book suitable for every-body in any situation. And yet, whatever the size and nature of a business, responsible management must understand at least the problems up to a point, just enough not to sign blank cheques for the fire officer but also not to throw out any vital recommendation purely because the cost appears to be excessive.

The idea of combustion seems simple enough. This despite the fact that virtually none of the known common fuels for fire do actually burn. What happens is that when organic compounds, like coal, wood, plastics and many others are heated, they only decompose to smaller molecules with greater volatility and flammability. Chemically, this process is known as *pyrolysis*. It is the fundamental explanation of nearly all phenomena that we term and regard as *fires*.

The process of pyrolysis releases gaseous materials which actually burn, create and feed the flames. (The heating of volatile liquid fuels produces a vapour which will burn readily well before pyrolysis would take place.) Such gases, driven by air currents, produce for example the 'fireballs' seen by witnesses of forest fires, aviation accidents and other fire spectaculars.

Fire can only occur or continue if three essentials – Heat, Fuel and Oxygen – are brought together. This can be represented by the triangle of fire.*

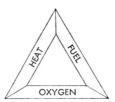

*Fire processes are in fact more complicated than the simple picture given by the Triangle of Fire. These processes, and also the mechanism by which certain types of extinguishing agent function, indicate that a fourth essential is necessary – chemical chain reactions. A pictorial representation can be made in the form

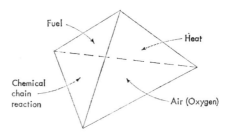

Removal of any one side destroys the triangle – removal of any one of the three essentials will extinguish the fire. Fire prevention and fire fighting are both based on this elementary principle: keep away or remove heat, fuel or oxygen, whichever may be most practicable in the circumstances.

In risk evaluation of various premises the *type of risk* (occupancy, work, climatic and other conditions, presence of fuels) and the *value* of anything (particularly human life) exposed to the hazard are assessed in relation to the presence of the three essentials necessary for fire, and the most suitable means for fighting fire should it occur.

Risk of death. If anything, mortality rates and the likelihood of lethal fires could be expected to shock people into defensive action. Unfortunately, they do not. It is known, for instance, that the risk of dying by fire is 70 per cent higher in Scotland than in England and Wales, yet householders and managers are yet to do anything truly decisive about it. (Poorer housing standards may be one of the causes of the greater risk. The climate demands more heating, perhaps the heating method ought to be revolutionized.)

M. A. North found that 'the chance of dying by fire varies

---

of a tetrahedron, a four-sided solid in which each side is a triangle and touches each of the other three sides.

If any side is broken the tetrahedron is destroyed. In reality if any of the four entities is removed from contact with the other three fire will not begin or continue. Thus fuel removal is the obvious method of fire prevention or extinction; fire can be extinguished by cooling, e.g. by water, or prevented by not allowing the temperature to rise; fires can be extinguished by smothering, preventing air from reaching the fire (e.g. a candle-snuffer or fire-blanket); fires can be prevented or extinguished by neutralizing the chemical chain reactions with negative catalysts such as halogenated hydrocarbons or chemical salts which form the basis of fire extinguishing dry powders.

A more extensive discussion of this subject is given in *The Extinguishment of Fire* by Walter M. Haessler, P.E., published by the National Fire Protection Association, 470 Atlantic Avenue, Boston, Massachusetts 02210, USA; in the *Fire Protection Handbook* also published by the NFPA; and in *Fire Technology Chemistry and Combustion* by Wharry and Hirst, published by the Institution of Fire Engineers, 149 New Walk, Leicester, LE1 7QB.

E

by region, age and sex, but the variation with age is predominant'.* Small children and old people are the most exposed to death by fire. Beyond the mere recognition of this rather obvious fact, the statistics ought to sound all alarm bells – but they do not. Homes with babies and the old do not enjoy increased fire protection though under the age of five the fatality rate is double the average, and over eighty-four the risk is ten times the average. Only 8 per cent of Britain's population are over sixty-nine, but they account for 43 per cent of the fire deaths. Once again the hazard is known, the risk can be evaluated properly – yet minor and major disasters are reported with sickening regularity. Perhaps society does not care enough to approve more drastic, i.e. more expensive, action. Perhaps it is just that the figures cannot shock a sufficient number of people although in Britain, 'the annual loss of life expectancy due to fire for the whole of the population is about 25,000 years'.†

In the same way as the Press judges the news value of a fire report (the more fatalities, the bigger the headline), the public in general as well as householders, industrial managers and business executives in particular, tend to be shocked only by infernos which wipe out a large number of people in one go. (In another field, the classic example of this attitude was the Vietnam war. As the hostilities went on and on, losing news value, the reports could demand space only according to the number of fatalities in a single action or on a particular day. That one by one, two by two, company by company, more people were killed gradually than in the 'spectaculars' made no difference to editors or readers.)

Unfortunately, risk evaluation by shock alone is not the most satisfactory method. In 1974, the special risk to lives in old folk's homes received urgent attention – *after* the fire at the Fairfield, in Edwalton, near Nottingham, where smoke killed

The Risk of Dying by Fire, Fire Research Note 981, Fire Research Station, 1973.

†S. J. Melinek: *Loss of Life Expectancy due to Fire, Fire Research Note 978*, Fire Research Station, 1973.

eighteen people aged between sixty-seven and ninety-one. The above average hazards there were well known. Many had mobility problems, various stages of deafness affected others, most of them needed sedatives to help them through the nights.

The Committee of Inquiry found no fundamentally new hazard: complacency emerged as the chief culprit. Fairfield had no automatic smoke detectors, its alarm was hand operated and not linked to a fire station, there was only one member of the staff on night duty with one other being 'on call', and the building itself, though only thirteen years old, had recognizable, inherent fire risks – ceilings that lacked fire resistance, roof voids and cavities without firestops. These risks were further exaggerated by the occupants themselves: it would have been impossible to stop them smoking in bedrooms and beds (the cause of the fire) without the confiscation of smoking materials and imposition of a humiliating institution atmosphere. The Inquiry concluded that without such Draconian measures and/ or excessive fire precaution expenditure (reducing the building programme) some degree of risk would always have to be accepted in homes for the elderly – even if architects received better fire training and more adequate guidance from the Department of Health, and if the fire hazards were designed out of this award-winning, prefabricated building system. (Only twelve days before the tragedy, Fairfield failed to qualify for the local council's new 'crash programme' to improve fire precautions in several dangerous homes for the elderly.)

Thus the *type of occupancy* of any premises is a key factor of risk evaluation. Fairfield, for example, would have represented entirely different categories of risk if it were used as offices, a school, hospital laboratories or store rooms.

Apart from the fatality and injury risks, the probabilities of the number of fires and the magnitude of likely losses and damages in a certain kind of occupancy are the chief components of the hazard assessment. These, in turn, are influenced by the kind of usage of the building, the work and other activities carried on, the sources of ignition which would normally be present, and the flammability of the materials stored or used in the premises.

As a basic rule of thumb, it can be said on the basis of statistical assessments that the death risk in the home is similar to those in buildings of most manufacturing industries (with the timber and furniture, and, above all, the chemical and petro-chemical industries being the chief exceptions). Some special occupancy risks will be dealt with elsewhere, but on the whole, the risk in hospitals appears to be above that in the home; those employed in agriculture and forestry are even more exposed; and according to various sets of statistics, hotels and motels are among the worst fire-security risks. (In a Western country people are eleven times more likely to be involved in a hotel fire than in a blaze in the home; the estimated death rate ranges from ten to twenty times those in the home. This is not because there are more fires in hotels, but because people are strangers and mostly asleep there during the major out-breaks.)

On the whole it seems a reasonable assessment to divide various occupancies into four categories concerning the severity of the general fire risk:*

Ordinary Fire Risks

Factories and workshops (except those listed below under more serious risks)

Blocks of flats

Breweries

Hospitals (with the exceptions below)

Public houses, hotels (risks due to type of occupancy, not the death risk which is much more severe), clubs and refreshment rooms (with exceptions below)

Libraries

Offices (including betting shops)

Private residences

*Based on the list in the *Nu-Swift Book of Knowledge*, private publication of Nu-Swift International Ltd, 1971.

Public buildings

Schools and churches (a new exceptional arson hazard with increased juvenile vandalism may affect the ranking of schools as fire risks)

Shops (with exceptions below)

Serious Fire Risks

Bakeries

Canteens and kitchens in clubs, factories, hospitals, hotels, restaurants, refreshment rooms and public houses

Department stores

Farms

Places of entertainment (e.g. cinemas, theatres, circuses, bingo halls and some clubs)

Printers

Severe Fire Risks

Distilleries

Dry cleaners

Fried-fish shops

Garages

Hospital dispensaries, laboratories, operating theatres

Ironmongers and stockists of paraffin

Laundries

Businesses which use, manufacture or store highly flammable materials (including liquids and gases) that appear under the classification of fires according to the main materials involved

Very Severe Fire Risks

Businesses which use, manufacture or store some extremely flammable materials such as carbon disulphide, nitro-cellulose, magnesium, etc.

A review of the *sources of ignition* is another essential part of risk evaluation. The presence of any such source increases the likelihood of a fire – any combination of these makes the hazard all the more serious.

With some sweeping generalization, two major groups of heat sources could be identified:

(1) the direct burning ones (including anything from cigarette ends to welding equipment); and

(2) other, non-burning sources such as friction produced by rapidly moving parts of machinery, electricity, spontaneous combustion – and, of course, explosions, although these are mostly the result rather than the cause of non-malicious fires.

Fire statistics may help to spotlight the most common of these causes, but the investigation of fires – on which the causal reports are based – is still a far from perfect art, and so the figures may be somewhat misleading. Smoking materials, for instance, are thought to be a very major cause of fires. There may be, however, a case for revision of this view. The recent decrease of cigarette smoking (the 'no significant change' in cigarette consumption according to other reports) has not produced any reduction in the number of fires or the proportion of fires attributed to smoking materials.

Arson, already another major cause, is probably ready for a considerable upgrading in importance. While the number of fires started by children playing with matches might not have changed much over the years, there is a significant – and, unfortunately, often undetected – increase in devastating outbreaks due to malicious, intentional ignition engineered by people whose motivation ranges from the political to the insane, and who start fires out of sheer vandalism or merely to fight boredom. Plant security from intruders as well as arsonists on the inside is, therefore, crucial.

Other common, yet often underestimated, sources of ignition include faulty or misused electrical installations and appliances (unprofessional connections, arcing, faulty earthing, frayed wiring, overloading of powerpoints, etc.); heating appliances; faulty, overheating and sparking machinery; naked lights (workers with oxy-acetylene cutting equipment, welders, and maintenance staff with blowlamps playing a predominant role); and deliberate rubbish incineration. In homes, cooking, heating and electrical appliances are major sources, while at some places of work spontaneous combustion (in hay, for instance) can be a serious problem.

These sources start fires in three main ways: through arson, carelessness and true accidents many of which are, in fact, preventable and so attributable to a degree of negligence, lack of foresight, careless and irregular checking and maintenance.

The general risk can be greatly increased or eliminated by the *type of materials* used, stored or manufactured in a building. In addition, the materials – in conjunction with the sources of heat – determine the type of fire any ignition will lead to. Thus the identification of the presence of known dangerous substances in the neighbourhood of common ignition sources is a key to fire prevention. Examination of thousands of cases has revealed, for instance, that the most common and so the most likely materials to be first ignited in a very high proportion of fires include parts of electrical installations; waste, dust and rubbish (hence the vital role of good housekeeping); textiles, flammable liquids; paper, foam and other packing materials; easily combustible materials used in the building structure (e.g. wood, particularly if oil-soaked under machinery) and in the fixtures and fittings (e.g. plastics).

The American fire classification is useful and deserves more interest than it at present seems to receive. Its great advantage is that it automatically combines fuel types and essential fire-fighting techniques to put out such fires. The US system uses three basic classes:

Class A: common combustible materials where large quantities of water (or solutions containing a high proportion of water) are necessary to cool the blaze and quench the flames.

Class B: flammable liquids, greases and other materials which, when alight, require some blanketing method (the exclusion of air) to be applied by the firefighter.

Class C: fires in 'live' electrical equipment where it is essential, at least in principle, to use an electrically non-conductive extinguishing agent. (In practice, as will be seen elsewhere, experienced firefighters first disconnect the 'live' equipment if at all possible and so change the class of fire they have to face.)

In Britain four classes of fires are recognized on the basis of fuels involved.

Class A: fires involving wood, paper, textiles and other carbonaceous, cellulosic materials.

Class B: fires involving flammable liquids, such as petrol, fuel oil, kerosene, alcohols, paints; viscous materials like tars; and also solids, like wax and resins, which melt and turn into liquids when heated.

Class C: fires involving gases such as methane, hydrogen, ordinary household gas, acetylene, as well as liquefied gases, such as butane or propane, which are discharged as a jet.

Class D: fires involving combustible metals such as magnesium, aluminium, lithium, sodium, potassium, and also some radioactive metals like uranium.

In Europe some countries recognize a fifth class: fires involving electrical equipment. Today, however, due to the use of complex, sophisticated materials and the omnipresence of electricity, virtually all fires are turned into 'mixed risks' (two or more of the above fuel classes burning together) complicated by 'live' electrical installations.

Finally, although this is very much a specialist job, management or anybody else bent on self-defence can evaluate the risk by examining how quick and far-reaching the *spread of fire* can be before meeting serious obstructions which shield people trying to escape and which help to check the ultimate extent of the blaze and the eventual damage.

As a rule of thumb by generalization it can be said that fires like to go upwards. The basic fire pattern is an upward conical shape, rising and spreading at the open end, and usually pointing at the seat of the fire below – a useful clue for investigators. If highly flammable materials surround the fire, lateral spread may result even if the gap open to the flames is no more than a rat hole. Downward burns occur in special circumstances. In industry, if accelerant liquids are present, these penetrate and seep through gaps carrying the flames below their seat. In homes or department stores where curtains may be first ignited, wind or draught may play the flames over a limited floor area until holes are burnt and bits of burning textile material and wood drop through.

The principally upward trend is explained by the basic chemical process of pyrolysis – the fact that organic compounds only decompose when heated and it is the released gaseous material that burns and rises. The upward spread of the fire is then created by *convection*. The lateral spread is partly achieved by *conduction* to adjacent flammables, and partly by the rising hot gases meeting an obstruction: when they reach the ceiling, they spread out sideways in search of another opening upwards, and if they find their way into a duct (e.g. air conditioning) or a lift shaft (not properly enclosed) or a staircase (with permanent openings or wedged-open fire-doors), they carry the fire with incredible speed further and further up. The third way of fire spread is *radiation*: as the heat builds up, it radiates across open space, and when at the far end ignition temperature is reached, combustibles just burst into flames as if touched by a torch.

It is due to the combination of convection, conduction and radiation that large open spaces (halls, department stores, theatres, etc.) are particularly hazardous, and that voids in walls and open staircases may nurse major disasters. Limiting the spread of fire by structural and other means is thus a major task both for *fire protection* and *fire precaution* efforts, and if the review of a building reveals the lack of such fire obstructions, it increases the risk very considerably.

The relevant laws are chiefly concerned with the safety of lives. The requirements come under the above two headings – protection and precautions.

Laws, bye-laws and building regulations aim at providing *fire protection* through structural means. These are to ensure that the spread of any fire inside a building will be prevented or at least retarded so that the fire will not become uncontrollable and the building will not collapse – or at least neither of these will happen fast enough to prevent safe evacuation. Structural means are also designed to prevent an outbreak from spreading beyond the building first ignited so that the general conflagration of a building complex or even an entire area could be avoided.

These aims are served in many ways, including the creation of compartments separated by fire resistant obstacles (walls, doors); the strict requirement of giving external walls a predetermined duration of fire resistance; the sufficient separation of buildings; safe roof construction; and the use of materials which give a specified performance in even the most serious fire situations.

Fire precautions, subject to the actual risk, deal with the various aspects of evacuation itself. Some of the relevant regulations concern structural requirements for the main means of escape such as enclosed corridors and stairways, protected routes and exits. Others provide the preconditions and facilities for successful evacuation and self-defence. These include effective detector and alarm systems, emergency lighting, directional signs leading to fire exits, and basic firefighting equipment such as fire hoses and extinguishers. The third group of precautions deals with the human element itself: evacuation plans and drills, staff training, assignment of individual responsibilities, firefighting instructions – anything that can turn a panicky emergency into a cool, controlled, routine procedure.

The problem for industrial and business executives as well as household 'managers' is that very often, between the recognized risk and the legal minimum, there is still a deep and wide gulf that can be tackled only by a substantial financial bridge.

5
What is a Life Worth?

If the risk is known, the cost of protection must be proportionate to the protected value. But what is a life worth?

There have been many attempts at putting a monetary value on life. After aviation disasters, major law cases of accidental injury, events like the thalidomide tragedy, actuarial assessments had to be agreed – and the estimates (earnings potential, etc.) varied widely according to the methods and ideas applied.

In the course of a study for the Third London Airport the Roskill Commission valued a male life at £9300. In 1967 a Road Research Laboratory Report valued a life at £6000, and another report, four years later, almost trebled that figure. Also in 1971 the Home Office used the figure of £30,000 in a project examining the siting of fire stations. By 1972, some papers referred to £50,000 and undoubtedly the average value of human life is rising at breakneck speed with inflation.

Unfortunately, the law cannot answer the problem. The main purpose of legislation is to protect life, yet legislators must walk the tightrope between the two highly respected principles that human life is invaluable and that the demands made of citizens have to be only 'reasonable' because laws are not supposed to suffocate people's livelihood either. Add to this that lawmaking has not been – and will probably never be – automated to qualify for the rocket age, and we reach the current situation that legislation can only crawl behind the motorized undertakers.

Just to mention a few examples:

The old Cinematograph Act was suitably amended in 1929,

soon after the Paisley (Glen Cinema) disaster, in which seventy Scottish children lost their lives in a wild stampede of 800 towards barred exits; the Eastwood Mills fire at Keighley (eight deaths) in 1956 led to the Factories Act, 1961, introducing compulsory alarms, fire drills, escape routes, etc.; the Henderson's department-store fire opened the way to the Offices, Shops and Railway Premises Act of 1963; at the cost of nineteen lives in the Top Storey Club fire at Bolton, Lancashire, the Licensing Act, 1964, came into force; a Hertfordshire caravan fire that killed four children was followed by the portable oil heaters regulation – passed in record time, within six months after the tragedy – in 1962.

Another important, and in many ways classic, example was the introduction of the Fire Precautions Act, 1971, probably the most important modern fire law in Britain, right on the trail of yet another hotel disaster: on Boxing Day 1969 the Rose and Crown at Saffron Walden. This Tudor coaching inn was set alight probably by an overheating television set. The details were all too familiar: an alarm silenced by burnt wires, screaming people in the windows, daring and desperate descents down knotted sheets, leaps from the roof, escapers driven back by smoke in unprotected corridors, death within three feet of a locked fire-exit with the key hanging in a glass box next to the door . . .

The Rose and Crown was owned by Trust Houses, 'a company which . . . provided fire protection in excess of that demanded by regulations. Good regulations would have probably demanded protection in excess of that provided.'* Immediately after this fire the Warwickshire fire brigade organized a special fire precautions seminar for hotels. Out of 200 managers only seven accepted the invitation. This was, of course, partly understandable: at the time the British Hotels and Restaurants Association itself hotly disputed an FPA report made four months before the fire, denied that many hotels were dangerous fire risks, and claimed that the report was 'unnecessarily alarmist'.

*Fire, 1972, op. cit.

(That report demonstrated with numerous examples why in a Western country people were eleven times more likely to be involved in a hotel fire than in a blaze in the home. It showed the various special risks, the lack of proper staff training, escape facilities, alarm equipment and evacuation procedures, and it called special attention to the risk represented by television sets left plugged in for the night in public lounges as well as in bedrooms. This alarmist report was fully illustrated by the Rose and Crown inferno, only four months after publication.)

In the circumstances it is understandable that once the Fire Precautions Act of 1971 was passed, the first designation order for its application concerned hotels. The second designation order – hospitals – is about to be published at the time of this writing. Factories will not need any special designation order. During the crossing of the legal no-man's-land – between the Act and the various designation orders – if the risk is serious enough, e.g. in schools, the fire brigades have the right, under Section 10, to enforce precautions by obtaining a court order.

The Fire Precautions Act is the first designed specifically to foresee and forestall, rather than trail behind, disasters. Once a particular designation order is made, it overrides all other legislation relevant to that sector, and so, hopefully, it helps to clear up the dreadful mess fire legislation has become in most countries over the centuries of mending and amending. It also clarifies complicated legal positions such as those that used to affect hotels.

If a hotel had a ballroom, it needed music and dancing licences with certain fire precautions; it also needed a licence for its bar and its lounge with another set of fire requirements. Under the Public Health Act of 1936 local authorities were empowered to require – if they wished – certain means of escape in buildings where the second storey was more than twenty feet above the ground. So if the above hotel management was unlucky enough to be located in certain areas it would also have to comply with these regulations. Finally, for a complex like Summerland, or London's Mayfair Hotel, which also has a theatre, a Theatre Licence, with yet another set of fire precautions, would be required. The unfortunate manager had to deal with fire and local authorities, study numerous Acts – after all, his offices were to be controlled by the Offices, Shops and Railway Premises Act! – and then only hope for the best that he was well within the law.

Now the various licences still apply – to sell liquor or play music or have live entertainment – but at least the fire requirements are becoming clearer and more coordinated. And from the risk point of view coordination is the key word: the presence of a theatre (large open space with no compartmentation for a tightly packed crowd which is not familiar with the premises and which may include the very young and the very old) represents an excessive hazard not only to those within its own confined area, but also to all those who may be dining or dancing or sleeping right above, below or next to it. The level of special precautions should therefore apply to the entire complex. That is why today, if there are several degrees of risk areas, the highest requirements are usually applied to the whole building.

Apart from long-confused management, architects, too, welcomed the overdue and much-needed rationalization of what was known as the maze of 2000 overlapping and contradictory British fire regulations. The Royal Institute of British Architects has long complained about the varied regulations multiplied many times by haphazard and even more varied local interpretation of the laws. Now it would be totally unrealistic to expect the complete reconstruction of old buildings to satisfy the new regulations, but old hazards could somehow be compensated for by new measures of precautions – at least to some extent.

To what extent this can be done is still a bone of serious contention. Although, luckily, the new system enjoys uniformity in giving the power of enforcement to the fire brigades up and down the country, and although the basic training given to prevention officers is the same, there are already some inevitable complaints of varied local interpretation of the fire brigade powers and of the level of requirements.

Under the various building regulations there has been a great deal of known and suspected corruption in local government. 'Many architects and builders blame what they euphemistically call "political and commercial" pressures for many of the inadequacies. Although they will not say so publicly, they claim that corruption is one of the main reasons why potentially dangerous materials and techniques are used, and approved of, by local authorities.'* After many disasters, in fact, local fire, building and other authorities produced long lists of reasons for the fire, and discovered, virtually overnight, what could have been done to avert it – with most plausible explanations why it had not been done at the time.

With enforcement left to the fire brigades, the student of the subject already begins to hear tales of corruption or at least 'more sympathetic consideration to management problems' in some areas, and of undue harshness in others. But now at least the brigades are directed to act in a similar fashion according to a national code of guidance; the brigades can be required to explain why they omitted to make certain requirements (if after a serious fire, this is used by, say, a hotel manager as an excuse); and the brigades can require only what is reasonable (e.g. sometimes only torches to provide 'emergency lighting' suggested by the code), because their demands are subject to appeals.

Enforcement remains, nevertheless, a serious and sometimes quite insoluble problem. Without substantially increased funds and staff, the brigades had to take on a tremendous extra workload. An immediate, seemingly hopeless task was to deal with some 70,000 hotels and boarding houses in England and Wales, and a quite incredible performance, with calmness, was required from the brigades to cope at all. There had always been a chronic shortage in well-trained factory inspectors and it was quite common that once a factory had been visited, checked and suitably advised, the inspector would not return to the

*The *Times*, 10 August 1973.

same premises for about eleven years. The situation cannot grow much worse than that, but whoever becomes the inspecting authority, whatever is fought out and agreed to be 'reasonable and adequate', whatever penalties are introduced and however severely the courts judge individual cases, fire precautions cannot ultimately be effectively enforced by the authorities without the individual management's full cooperation and without the management's full responsibility for *maintaining* means of escape, alarms, firefighting equipment and other life- and property-saving measures as prescribed.

In this respect, once again, persuasion must play a vital role: management will spend money only if convinced that it is in a good cause, if the risk is fully known, if the consequences of a major fire are not only understood, but profoundly feared, too.

Some people are convinced that legislation is altogether the wrong way to go about fire precautions. They argue that once there is a law for anything, people will do their duty – but never any more. If there is a law, the natural human reaction is im- mediately to seek a loophole, a way to get around the regulation in the easiest and cheapest manner. They mention examples such as the necessity of self-closing doors: while the authorities stub- bornly refused to permit any means of temporary fastening of such doors (e.g. in corridors where heavy loads were carried regularly by labourers), the law was simply broken in the crudest possible fashion, by wedges, hooks, weights; since the doors can be kept open by a system linked to detectors or the alarm which automatically releases them to let the self-closing mechanism do its job, management can at least evaluate the risk, and decide logically whether investment or the enforce- ment of discipline is more justified.

Another example sometimes referred to is the problem of illegal child-minding. It was suggested that as many as a hundred thousand children were left regularly in the care (or carelessness?) of unregistered 'establishments' and this, apart from educational hazards, implied a serious fire risk to lives, too. A government-financed inquiry in 1974 found that London and other authorities started various schemes to advise, help, legalize and so, to some extent, control the secret child-minder. They introduced, for instance, the lending out of fireguards which is obviously a greater help to safety than the forcing of the quite ineradicable system further underground. In the Midlands and the North, however, the councils were found to be 'too ostrich-like' in the rigid application of the law, although (or perhaps as a result) the problem there was the most serious.

Against the hopelessness of blind law-enforcement a London fire prevention officer recalled a case he had to solve:

It was a large South London housing estate with four huge underground car parks. In various positions there were fire extinguishers, but these kept disappearing. Eventually we found ninety of them in a canal nearby. Obviously, kids had just chucked them into the water without even having the fun of discharging them first. Instead of replacing them again and again in their original positions, we simply put the new ones higher up the wall – out of the reach of the smaller and younger little rascal.

In the car parks we had another problem. The hundreds of tenants just couldn't care about fire problems. When the tenants' association organized an instruction session held by one of our officers, perhaps ten or fifteen people turned up to listen. Nobody ever reported any vandalism although there was plenty. The reels were always torn out of the wall, the drums twisted, hoses cut up, nozzles gone. We put in a few extinguishers – but that only introduced a new hazard in that particular situation: vandals took them upstairs and chucked them out of the window to see the explosion.

Then we had a brainwave: we took off the expensive, attractive nozzles from the new hose-reels, and then replaced the customary fire notices by others saying 'car wash-down tubing – replace after use'. We never had any more trouble. For one thing, it's not attractive, there is no glamour in playing with an ordinary garden hose – you can't play firemen with it, can you? Besides, when kids did try to have a go, tenants were now quick to throw them out by the scruff of the neck shouting 'it's ours! it's for the car! don't you ever touch it!' And we never had another loss or damage in that car-park.

F

Against mere law enforcement, and in favour of ultimate individual and/or managerial responsibility, the main argument is that beyond a certain point authorities simply cannot judge the true and full extent of the risk to property and even to life, and at that stage the application of cold logic, terms of cost-effectiveness and risk evaluation can produce pretty unpalatable yet hard-to-deny points of reasoning.

Hospitals are probably the best example.

In terms of actual hazard, some other types of buildings – hostels, for instance – represent a much greater threat to life, yet hospitals and the safety of patients are such an explosive issue that under the Fire Precautions Act these were given considerable priority to become the subject of the second designation order. The order was meant to be published in 1974, but the preparation of the code of guidance led to a great deal of inter-departmental argument and so delayed the application of the Act.

'Argument? What argument?!' exclaimed a zealous Member of Parliament, representative of a militant industrial electoral district, to whom this author happened to mention the problem. In a mood of true swashbuckling he decided to raise the question in the House, because he was convinced that this was 'yet another conspiracy by the doctors to ruin the system'. His view was that if the fire authorities suggest the necessity of certain measures the health authorities should jump to attention and provide the money for it. To his eternal good fortune he was advised to make some inquiries first before putting down a question. When he received the first few, rather complex facts of life, he argued that 'surely, those poor, helpless patients, exposed to risk in their infirmity, the old and the mentally weak, must receive absolute protection whatever the problems and whatever the cost of solution!' Soon, however, he was driven away from jumping to conclusions – even though in principle he was perfectly right. Why?

The simple answer is that there are considerable doubts about the advisability of unlimited expenditure on fire precautions in hospitals. An unofficial, private inquiry examined the situation in sample hospitals and reached the conclusion that it would cost something in the region of £102 million to upgrade Britain's hospitals to the letter of the fire regulations. For that sum, at the time, six new general hospitals could have been built. In those additional hospitals, thousands could have received quicker and better treatment, and an untold number of patients could have been saved. In the cold light of logical assessment the question was reduced to this simple form: would better precautions or more hospitals save more lives? Or, if it must be put that way: which omission would cause more deaths?

Despite the occasional fire tragedies that kill patients (like the one in Coldharbour Hospital at Sherborne, Dorset, where thirty people died in 1972), statistical examinations reveal that the extra risk is mostly matched by extra protection, and the chance of death from fire is still no greater in hospitals than in private dwellings. That argues against excessive expenditure. On the other hand, a hospital patient relies on others, the authorities, to protect him, and – as in the case of bus/train/ air services *v.* private cars argument – he can reasonably expect a higher degree of safety and protection when in the care of a public service than in his own home.

It is therefore within these limits that the risk must be reviewed, and the value of a life must be determined, before the right protective measures are decided.

Some health authorities complain that the fire brigades 'are new to this hospital game' and try to 'apply experience gained in hotels to hospitals where some of their suggested precautions are just too ridiculous for words'. Fire-prevention officers are sometimes too ready to suggest sprinkler systems for general wards where not only the installation cost but also the risk of unnecessary, accidental drenching of patients is unjustifiable.

Another important point which fire officers find hard to accept concerns evacuation. Health authorities first had to convince architects that building a hospital was more a matter of planning, based on the recognition of systems and the study of hospital dynamics, than a pure design task. Staircases, for instance, must 'earn their keep' in everyday use as well as adding to the level of safety. Firemen tend to favour enclosed, well-protected staircases because they have plenty of experience with them – and have seen many tragedies when these good vertical escape facilities were missing from factories, hotels, high-rise buildings. On the other hand, bedbound patients with a dependence on certain drips may survive an exceptionally long horizontal evacuation run rather than a cumbersome move down the stairs however well within the advisable travel distance the protected route down may be found. This, of course, necessitates greater horizontal protection – compartmentation.

Inside large wards part of the fire protection may be based on the same principle as nursing itself: all the thirty or more patients can easily be kept under observation at all times even by a small number of staff. Unfortunately, once there is a fire, the lack of compartmentation is an additional hazard. Modern nursing ideas, however, tend to favour the breaking up of large wards into bays that contain about six beds each. If the separation is fire-resistant, this arrangement advances fire precautions, but at the same time, reduces observation and limits the range of the best fire detectors, the human eyes. So the answer may be the introduction of heat or smoke detectors which, in turn, could also control the self-closing doors with which the fire brigades want to break up the endless hospital corridors. Since they accept the temporary fastening of these doors by magnetic catches if the magnets are released automatically each time the sensors detect excessive heat or smoke, fire-prevention officers see no good reason why such doors should not be made compulsory and why any other fastening, like wedging, should be outlawed.

'Which leaves us with a hell of a problem,' health authorities answer. 'Hospitals are not compelled to accept the firemen's advice, but who can take the risk of refusing it? The main guidance issued by the Ministry, Hospital Technical Memorandum No. 16, does not make the use of these doors compulsory. Nurses hate the self-closing doors because they make their work more difficult, and cause delays and inconvenience when, for instance, wheeling patients along. Engineers object to those doors because they are heavy and damage easily. Management committees dislike the sensor-controlled doors because the installation is expensive, each door needs two magnetic catches and two extra detectors to operate them, and finally the choice is between costly maintenance programmes and sixteen false alarms for each true one. Therefore it is easy to see why hospitals may be reluctant to spend much on those doors – they deprive the health service of much-needed funds for treatment.'

It is, of course, way beyond the scope of this book even to pretend a serious quest for a complete and satisfactory answer, but hospitals certainly help to demonstrate the complexity of a particular fire-precaution problem and the numerous possible approaches that may lead to a solution. When, for example, this author put these various health authority views to some fire prevention specialists, further intriguing points emerged.

One of their main complaints was that although the complexity of the hospital problem necessitated the employment of top-flight fire-prevention experts who would have the duty and opportunity to specialize in and understand all sides of the problem, and although the guidelines issued to hospital boards clearly demanded the appointment of such officers, in most areas 'the salary offered in advertised vacancies was often inadequate to attract top men. The salary level also suggested that the selected man would not enjoy all the authority he would need for doing a satisfactory job.' (Apparently, the salary level did not need a substantial increase because 'it was fairly easy to fill these jobs as they came up'. The question was: were the vacancies filled by the right men? Usually, the age of the applicant was not specified and so many retired fire officers were interested. This did not necessarily mean that hospitals could successfully compete with industry or hotel chains for the best qualified specialists.)

Another point they raised concerned equipment. Although most regions follow the centrally issued recommendations, there can be no real standardization because the various areas and even individual hospitals purchase their own equipment and they do not have to accept any central guidance. According to some specialists, hospitals tend to select the cheapest available equipment because 'only some posh private establishments like abortion clinics can afford to choose by other criteria'. The differences that occur in equipment and even alarm systems only aggravate the serious problem of dangerously insufficient staff training in hospitals. (See next chapter.)

Beyond all these and other similar considerations a statistical examination could produce a different approach by pinpointing the main hazards and the most likely victims, and thus directing limited resources towards the most effective ways of utilization.

'Let's face it,' said an embittered engineer who must live with the fire risk in hospitals, 'we lose on average something like fifteen patients a year. Most of these are lost in the occasional really big fires, like the Shelton mental hospital, where the greatest mistake exposed by the disaster concerned staff training, alarm and evacuation procedures. To reduce or even halve the annual fire deaths in hospitals would not justify the sort of investment, a hundred million pounds, that would be necessary to achieve really meaningful all-round improvement of safety.

'On the other hand, we already know quite a lot about the main hazards. We know that most of the fire fatalities we suffer occur among the old and the mentally handicapped. This would suggest the reinforcement of our defences mainly in mental hospitals and geriatric wards. This kind of thinking will soon become more important than ever before, because the modern approach is the introduction of mental and geriatric units in general hospitals rather than continued isolation in specialist hospitals. It would be better for the patients, and we would find staff more easily for those wards than for mental homes and the like. After all, not many people like to nurse nothing but geriatric and mental cases.'

Such de-segregation will, of course, increase the risk for general hospitals and, as in the case of hotels incorporating ballrooms and theatres, the safety of the whole mixed risk would have to be considered as precarious as the most hazardous link in the chain.

Fortunately, statistical examinations have already indicated the area where resources could be used most effectively* – which makes it even more regrettable that extra funds have not yet been made available for initiating urgent additional research and that industry has not been induced to study the subject and make (to them potentially very profitable) proposals.

When the records of mental and other hospitals were compared, it was found that the chance of fatalities and not the general fire risks or frequency of outbreaks was greater in mental hospitals. A major difference that transpired was in the sources of ignition: smoking and malicious origins dominated the causal statistics in mental hospitals and geriatric wards, thus pinpointing an old, mentally handicapped chain-smoker (who would probably light up secretly, against the strictest regulations, in bed at night, perhaps under the blanket) as a special risk.

In mental hospitals, fire occurred more frequently in wards and less frequently in kitchens than in other hospitals . . . indicating once again that patients were the main risk.

Among the materials first ignited, bedding materials figured rather prominently and together with other textiles, clothing and upholstery accounted for about a quarter of the fires. An examination of fatalities was even more rewarding: in most cases, deaths occurred only if bedding materials, clothes and upholstery were ignited first or early on in the outbreak. It was discovered† that the structure of the buildings in those lethal

*e.g. S. E. Chandler: *Fires in Hospitals, F.R. Note 831,* 1970, or M. A. North and R. Baldwin: *Fire Risks in Hospitals, F.R. Note 983,* 1973.
†North and Baldwin, op. cit.

fires played no important part and therefore stricter fire regulations for building structures would not have reduced the number of fatalities.

If, however, 'patients' bedding and clothing could be made flame-resistant, the number of fatal fires might have been reduced by 70 per cent and the number of deaths by 40 per cent, presuming that the new materials did not increase the smoke or toxic gas hazard. . . . If it were possible to eliminate fires which ignited bedding, clothing or upholstery, the number of fatal fires would be reduced by 80 per cent and the number of deaths by 90 per cent', preventing more than a dozen deaths a year.

Now, at last, we are not talking about investments in the hundred million category – yet because of the low number of fire deaths even the much smaller expenditure required for such research fails to achieve sufficient priority.

Health authorities seem to accept with resignation that although there is some promising research being conducted in the United States, the suitably cheap and practicable flame-resistant material for patients' clothing and bedding has not yet been found, and the proposition is not yet economic enough for the Health Service to invite competitive bids from industry. This is difficult to accept because the solution would not only reduce the number of fatalities and protect patients from themselves, but would also reduce the severity of fires, minimize the losses, and even save money on rendering some other fire-protection measures superfluous.

The Hospital Technical Memorandum No. 16 makes some rather discouraging reference to this problem:

'. . . 59. Fabrics made from cotton, linen or viscose rayon are flammable and contribute significantly to the general fire risk in a hospital. A flame-resistant process (PROBAN) is available, which is effective for the life of the item, provided the laundering instructions, that the material is not boiled or bleached or starched and that soapless detergents only are used where water is not zero hardness, are carefully followed.' This process is not cheap and creates obvious problems hospitals find

Bad housekeeping prevents access to the weapons of fire defence, tends to damage extinguishers, punctures hoses, blocks nozzles with dirt. *London Fire Brigade*

Water type, gas pressure extinguisher for fires involving carbonaceous materials such as wood, textiles, paper and straw (Class A). Extinguishment is obtained by cooling.

Foam type, gas pressure extinguisher for fires involving flammable liquids such as petrol, oils, paraffin, white spirit, paints and cooking fats (Class B). Extinguishment is obtained mainly by smothering.

BCF extinguisher mainly fires involving live electric equipment and motor veh small flammable liquid an gas fires (Classes B & C) and small solid carbonace fires (Class A). Extinguish is obtained by smothering and by inhibition of the processes of combustion.

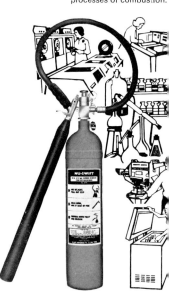

Stored pressure dry powder extinguisher for fires involving flammable liquids (Class B), flammable gases (Class C) and live electrical equipment. Extinguishment is obtained by inhibition of the processes of combustion

Carbon dioxide extinguisher for indoor fires involving delicate electrical and electronic equipment and medium quantities of flammable liquids (Class B). Extinguishment is obtained by displacement of air.

Stored pressure multipurpose dry powder extinguisher for all common types of fires, including 'mixed risks'. Classes B and C fires and flames of Class A fires are extinguished by inhibition of the processes of combustion. The burning solids of Class A fires are extinguished by impregnation and encrustation.

Above left, Trapped. Those who reach this fire exit will find no way out. Those behind will pile on top of them

Above, Trapped. Those who try to escape down this way will run into an inferno

Trapped. An arsonist could not have made better arrangements to guide people into a tight corner. *London Fire Brigade* difficult to cope with. It 'reduces slightly the tear strength of the fabric' and it is more difficult to remove stains from such treated sheets, needing quick soaking in cold water and the use of synthetic detergents soon after soiling.

Another method, not yet evaluated, is to use specially treated fibres which have flame resistance like wool, but there is an additional risk of severe burns from molten synthetic fibres, and the special treatment remains effective only if special laundering methods are used.

'. . . 65. There may be some justification for expenditure on flame-resistant bedclothes for certain patients in e.g. psychiatric, mentally subnormal and geriatric wards', but soiling and staining is an acute and frequent problem just there, and laundering may prove to be an impossible obstacle. 'Satisfactory flame-resistant cotton sheeting is not available at present' – treatment must be repeated in the laundry after each wash.

Apart from the troublesome laundry problems, flame-proofing today is a matter of cost. Invented about five years ago, a non-burning, inherently flame-proof nylon material is available, for instance, for racing drivers' overalls, socks and underwear, but it is still very expensive. Sheets made of such fabric cost between five and ten times more than ordinary ones. There are flame-resistant, self-extinguishing curtain materials (used by hotels) and the flame-resistant material for children's nighties became considerably cheaper as soon as vast sales potential was virtually guaranteed by the recent introduction of a law to protect children.

Thus, apart from the logical process of problem-recognition, fact-finding exercises, publicized deductions and calculation of cost-effectiveness, we must wait once again for the tragedy that can set the legal machinery in motion. Or is it only that although some spectacular tragedies are already on record and available to supply the necessary impetus if somebody wished to use them for that purpose, the authorities must wait for more tragedies and a greater public outcry (like in the case of numerous theatre disasters) to start the wheels turning?

Foamed plastics are known to be a tremendous fire hazard and an outright risk to lives. In 1972 G. Connell of the Factory Inspectorate and the Glasgow Fire Brigade joined forces to demonstrate the dangers to upholstery manufacturers. Some seventy foamed plastic cushions – 'such as might be found in even a small upholstery factory' – were ignited in order to show why extensive precautions were recommended for premises where such materials were used. Within fifteen seconds the ground floor of a derelict warehouse was swallowed by dense black smoke, and another fifteen seconds later smoke was pouring out of upper windows, too. The toxicity of the fumes was such that those who had not escaped virtually within the first few seconds, would have died in there despite the immediate assistance available from the fire brigade. Firemaster G. P. Cooper of the Glasgow brigade 'said that nobody was suggesting that foam plastics should be banned or anything like that, but the risk had to be learned to be lived with'.* His advice to anyone involved was that if such a fire seemed to be beyond control, 'Run! Don't wait for anything. Just run. And call the fire brigade.'

Sound advice, no doubt, to everyone who can judge when a fire seems 'to be beyond control' and to those who can 'just run' because they are not bedridden and not asleep (in a hospital or a hotel, for example). Illustrative disasters are readily available to interested parties. In 1968 in the James Watt Street fire of Glasgow most of the twenty-two fatalities were caused by suffocation due to fumes from burning plastic foams. When the Department of Employment and the Furniture, Timber and Allied Trades Union studied the speedy burning of and poisonous gases from polyurethane foam (widely used in furniture, car seats and insulation), the union's deputy general secretary accused the Home Office of four years of 'monstrous inactivity' and inability 'to face up to the problem'.† Since then, more cases have gone on record. Mothers and their babies as well as

*Fire, June 1972.
†Sunday Mirror, 19 March 1972.

healthy, grown-up hotel guests suffocated by such fumes. The twenty-four women who died in the Shelton mental hospital fire were also victims of the little-publicized killer: a cigarette dropped on a chair with polyurethane foam cushions. (In addition to the already mentioned shortcomings of staff training and alarm procedures, the victims were specially exposed, presumably, by being incapable of recognizing at what point the fire was 'beyond control' and of 'just running' away to save themselves.)

If, as it was reported at the time, the Home Office cannot do anything about the use of polyurethane, if such materials cannot be outlawed and so older chairs and mattresses may remain in private homes as well as in hotels and hostels (responsible hotels now install mainly the flame-resistant, self-extinguishing kind), at least the most exposed in public care – the old and the mentally sick – should be protected compulsorily. For such a measure would probably be justifiable even financially as something commensurate with the risk and compatible with the principal *raison d'être* of hospitals.

With these numerous aspects in mind, it appeared reasonable to accept – as recommended by recent fire investigations, e.g. after the Coldharbour hospital fire – that it would be sensible to invest more heavily in detector and alarm systems, above all in areas where patients and their activities cannot be seen by others (mainly staff) at least once in every six minutes. Such equipment would be most useful in psychiatric and geriatric wards, particularly if these were located at an unusually great distance from fire stations, on the moors for instance.

But health authorities also recognize that more automatic installations may lead to more false alarms, sending more fire engines on wild-goose chases and reducing the availability of pumps and the speed of fire brigade response to calls. Therefore, further self-help is required – particularly in the light of the statistical evidence indicating that even with inadequate equipment and with imperfect training of staff, a high proportion of fires have been extinguished before the arrival of the fire brigade.

As S. E. Chandler, compiler of the table opposite, pointed out, hospitals seemed to have a higher 'extinction before arrival of fire brigade' success rate than other buildings. One of the reasons could be that because of the risks involved, hospitals called brigade assistance more readily than others, even to trivial outbreaks and another explanation might have been that irrespective of equipment quality and staff training level, the mere availability of extinguishing equipment induced and facilitated remarkably effective firefighting.

In 1968, for instance, there were 684 fires in hospitals. Almost half of these occurred in mental hospitals. Of the 684, 556 were tackled in some ways before the arrival of professional assistance, and this amateur firefighting not only helped to reduce the spread of the outbreaks, but also scored outright successes in almost four out of every five cases.*

('Allowed to burn out' is not a particularly good or satisfactory method of firefighting, but for statistical purposes it must be regarded as 'success' because the fire is out, indeed, before the arrival of the brigade. The relatively high rate of success of simpler means – e.g. buckets or beating – is due to the fact that these are applied to the smallest fires and mishaps, such as cigarettes smouldering on carpets, where they can hardly fail.)

The advantage and imperative necessity of human preparedness for immediate self-defence are increasingly recognized by management, unions and the law. Yet, oddly enough, individual householders seem to value human lives the least.

Although in Western countries, about two-thirds of the annual fire deaths occur in the home with the very old and the very young being the most exposed, especially when left alone in the house, very few heads of families are willing to think positively about the risk, and even fewer will actually do anything about better protection. Although fires in private dwellings may be

*S. E. Chandler, op cit.

Methods of firefighting in hospital fires before the arrival of the fire brigade (1968)

Method	Total	Success-fully exting-uished	Not exting-uished	% of success
Extinguishers	160	100	60	62·5
Water from buckets, immersion	112	92	20	82·1
Beating, smothering	52	40	12	76·9
Removal	40	32	8	80·0
Allowed to burn out	24	24	—	100·0
Other small non-chemical means	40	40	—	100·0
Two or more of above methods	24	16	8	66·7
More powerful methods (mainly internal hose reels/hydrants)	104	52	52	50·0
TOTAL	556	396	160	77·2

a threat to neighbours, governments must respect the freedom of the individual – the freedom of remaining careless, thoughtless and negligent – and the law cannot enforce fire prevention in the home. Parents can be prosecuted only in some special circumstances, e.g. the death of a child due to accident with an insufficiently guarded fire.

Automatic fire detection would cost about £250 or more for a private house, and sprinkler protection would be several times more expensive. Therefore these are impracticable propositions. Fire extinguishers are incomparably cheaper, yet even these cost a great deal more than individual householders appear to be willing to spend on additional safety for the family.

This author conducted a very limited and haphazard survey

in London and Sheffield. The result cannot be regarded as representative in any sense – due to reasons such as the smallness of the sample, etc. – but it is perhaps not insignificant that out of 187 householders/heads of families, less than 20 per cent were 'willing to consider spending £10 or more' on additional means of protection, however effective the investment may prove to be. The main argument against expenditure was 'the unlikeliness of ever having a fire'. The sad significance of this is increased by the fact that the sample, unlike in proper opinion polls, was not selected at all to cover various social-educational-income groups: more than 80 per cent of the people asked were in the 'over £3000 a year' and most of these in the 'over £4000 a year' income bracket, with the majority being university-educated professionals.

(A somewhat impromptu survey at the Fire Research Station* found that people could rank risks fairly accurately, but the hazard of anybody being in the home if and when it catches fire was underestimated; the implied values of life ranged from £17,000 to £55,000; the average sum people appeared to be willing to spend to reduce the existing risk to a tenth was £17·9 per household. Yet many of these belonged to probably the most fire-conscious group of the population, because the questionnaire was answered by visitors of the Fire Research Station Open Days.)

The general unpreparedness of the private dwelling is reflected not only by the fact that very few have some basic firefighting equipment (less than 10 per cent are thought to own extinguishers and/or other means, e.g. an asbestos blanket, to smother fires), but also by the available evidence that half the people in burning houses do not even attempt to fight an outbreak. When they try anything, they achieve most with water and fail even with the best equipment because they simply do not know how to make use of it. Yet when this author asked those 187 householders if they had ever seen and/or gone

*S. J. Melinek, Sara K. D. Woolley and R. Baldwin: *Analysis of a Questionnaire on Attitudes*, F.R. *Note 962*, Fire Research Station, 1973.

through carefully a *safety in the house* type check-list, the answers were shattering: almost 70 per cent had never seen a check-list; only 10 per cent had ever read such a list carefully; and a mere 4 per cent claimed to have examined fires, electrical installations, the storage of matches away from small children, the preparedness of the wife for fires, etc., according to a check-list like those issued by the local fire brigade or the Fire Protection Association.

Whatever the distortion produced by a small improvised poll like this, the implications are strongly supported by the daily ration of minor and major tragedies in which people can do little or nothing to save themselves. So our true assessment of human lives is represented by the carelessness of the do-it-yourself electrician, by the rarity value of those who shut the doors in the house and unplug the television set for the night, by the continued usage of unsafe and old-fashioned oil-heaters in, for instance, draughty corridors, and by the level of ignorance displayed by those who have to face 'just an ordinary fat pan fire'. (Out of a hundred cases, only ten such fires were put out the correct way of smothering with a lid or cloth – preferably glass-fibre cloth. A third of the people involved used water, one of the most dangerous methods, despite constant advice against it, and there were fifteen who virtually asked for injury: they tried to carry the burning pan out of the kitchen.)

If we recognize that people are reluctant to 'invest' just a few minutes of their time in reading and accepting some advice, it becomes perhaps more understandable that they refuse to spend actual cash on self-defence. Apart from the general education of the public – that will, hopefully, begin in all schools – a new piece of legislation will probably help to convince people about the value of life and about their own ability to defend themselves: probably for the first time everybody, and not only management, will be involved in self-defence at places of work.

Until now, it was left to management alone to carry out what the law required and it depended on their sensible attitude and goodwill to do any more than that. While unions often demanded better and safer working conditions, they hardly ever took any interest in fighting for greater safety at places of work, and it appears to be an almost impossible task to trace any case of strike against some fire hazard. In North-West London there was once a strike threat in a factory when a series of offices was created by putting up partition walls. Eventually it turned out that the fire issue was only to support a most trivial work-demarcation dispute and as soon as this was settled the subject of fire hazard was dropped and forgotten. Fire-prevention officers always give immediate, sympathetic attention to any complaints from employees – even anonymous reports of, say, blocked exits, are investigated – but often they find that the informers had been dismissed by the managements or bear some other grudge against the alleged fire offender.

The new Health and Safety at Work Act, in force from April 1975, is the most revolutionary legislation ever since the Factory Act laid down measures to safeguard mill machinery in 1844. Apart from charging management with tremendous responsibility for all employees' health and safety at work, and apart from sensibly reorganizing the supervision and coordination of various safety measures, it also gives legal rights to unions and workers' safety representatives to play an active part in creating safer conditions. In order to ensure everybody's wholehearted participation in safety measures, not only employers but also employees can be fined quite heavily for offences under the Act.

Because all aspects of health and safety will have to be considered together (safe processes with safe equipment to be used in a safe manner in safe buildings), law enforcement representatives – factory inspectors and fire-prevention officers – will have to consult one another, work closely together, and avoid giving contradictory instructions which, for example, may introduce a more accident-free work process but create a new fire hazard or obstruct an escape route. To ensure the fire safety of a *place*, supervision of proper alarms, evacuation and staff drill is the fire authority's responsibility. The factory inspectors of the new Health and Safety Executive look after the *process*, check that the equipment and the method of work do not create fire hazards and explosion, and ensure that the management properly trains all employees for the correct, safe and fire-free execution of duties.

General repair and maintenance, frequent causes of devastating fires, will probably have to be singled out for special attention, particularly because such works have long been in a safety no-man's-land. The problem was fully illustrated in a recent case at a factory that used liquid butane containers. The fire authority had inspected and approved the premises, alarms, evacuation routes and procedures. Factory inspectors checked the two production lines, approved the pipes and the valves and the containers, storage of inflammable materials, manner of operations, etc.

Then one day twenty-three girls continued, quite properly, working on one production line while the maintenance men carried out some minor repairs on the parallel second production line. The men had to disconnect some pipes and, unknown to them, somebody turned on a valve way down the line. This was an error, creating a hazard, but no immediate fire. Liquid butane began to flow out, all over the floor, with gas accumulating fast above. The alarm was properly sounded and, according to the well-planned fire drill, the production line was brought to a halt while the girls began evacuation. Part of the stoppage was to switch off an electric motor. The switch was only two feet (60 cm) from the floor and it sparked almost invisibly. There was an instant ignition and the place was ablaze from end to end. All the girls were injured, though, luckily, none of them was killed.

To investigators it was obvious that there should have been warning notices on the various valves to prevent anybody turning on the gas supply when pipes were disconnected for maintenance. But actual ignition could have been foreseen only by better coordination between supervising authorities: it was not for the fire officer to know that the switch was not flame-

G

proof and that in the circumstances it would have been wiser to place it some eight feet (2·5 m) above the floor; and it was not for the factory inspector to know that the fire alarm and evacuation procedure would involve switching off motors every time, perhaps in a situation where gas flowed freely everywhere.

Another classic example of the coordination problem occurred in London. Nine out of twelve fire alarms in a large council building were found to be out of action. Cause: corrosion. Maintenance people were told off, repairs were carried out, and because the equipment was relatively new, an odd case of corrosion was recorded. Six months later, another test found most alarms out of action once again. The cause was discovered purely by chance: the persistent discharge of chlorine from a nearby factory, i.e. pollution, created this unusual hazard to life. To foresee and prevent a case like this, even those who specialize in pollution problems would have to keep the innumerable aspects of the fire hazard in mind.

Under this new Act, our valuation of human life will be examined and re-examined in many ways. For example, when every employer, even the self-employed, becomes legally responsible for safety in general, window-cleaners' ladders will have to be fully secured to the wall – or another man must hold it at all times. Will people be ready to pay the double cost? In some factories, where the risk is 'marginal', employers may have to enforce 'no smoking' regulations. Will additional safety be welcome by all smokers?

But the greatest test of all will come in the field which is most frequently neglected, often ridiculed or simply overlooked, which is, nevertheless, the key to self-defence – training. Will management make people duly available? Will available people attend training sessions in spirit as well as putting in a physical appearance? Will there be enough and well-enough trained instructors available?

6
Gentlemen Do Not Burn

Until quite recently most airlines simply refused to ask passengers to wear safety belts during flights. Although they knew perfectly well that turbulence, particularly the unforeseeable clear-air kind, could cause numerous injuries and even fatalities, the companies thought that they must not frighten away their customers by calling attention to hazards. Some airlines still ask us to 'wear seat belts whenever seated *for comfort*'.

Not very long ago, an international airline insisted on covering the emergency exit markings with curtains for 'the sake of our passengers' mental comfort'; and it was common practice not to distribute newspapers on board if they made any reference to aviation mishaps.

It is the mentality of the ostrich as well as that of an enlightened Hungarian king who in the eleventh century refused to believe in witches, and ruled in Latin that the witches who did not exist must never be mentioned. (*'De strigis quae non sunt nulla questio fiat.'*) As if silence would drive away turbulence, the fear of witches and, of course, the fire hazard.

If this atmosphere of general disbelief in 'that it may happen to us, too', were not enough to maintain our ill-founded optimism, and keep us from partaking in one of those 'ridiculous fire drills', there would still be a peculiar social stigma attached to fire training because, as a butler in a stately home once informed the local fire chief: 'Better people burn only at the stake – not in bed.'

Like airlines of the past, some 'top' department store and hotel staff still refuse to admit the existence of any degree of risk in their classy establishments. When two fire engines were brought to a screeching halt in front of Claridge's, an imperturbable doorman walked up to the officer in charge and asked 'Can I help you, sir?' The officer had no time for him, and answered while running towards the entrance: 'You have a fire here!' The doorman knew how to recognize an ordinary mortal when he saw one, so he just smiled and declared: 'You must be mistaken, sir. We do not have fires at Claridge's. Sir.'

At Lambeth fire station they still cherish the memory of a call from the Savoy. A cool voice reported a fire in the kitchen of the hotel and instructed: 'Will fire engines please respond to the back entrance.' Later a member of the management explained that although, admittedly, it meant quite a detour, and firemen then had a longer run to the fire, it was 'simply unimaginable to have the main entrance obstructed by those monstrous vehicles'.

If gentlemen do not have fires, and if management is frequently and rightly criticized for lack of cooperation in fire matters and for even refusing to release employees for instruction, it cannot be argued that staff have shown an excessive interest in the problem.

Now, in the wake of the Health and Safety at Work Act, attitudes may begin to change at last . . . at least at the top. The TUC is anxious to revitalize the work safety committees and give them authority. (Until now, senior managers were hardly ever involved. If decisions were taken, these were largely ignored, and so it became obvious to all that the committee was only a 'talking shop'. Workers knew too little of safety matters and even of the very existence of the committees, although as long ago as 1969 9487 joint committees had already been established to cover some 70 per cent of the work force in factories with more than fifty employees, and the number of committees then increased sharply everywhere in anticipation of the new legislation.)

The unions run various free one- or two-week courses, evening and weekend seminars to acquaint full-time officials as well as shop stewards with health and safety matters, so that they can, in turn, train others. The TUC believes that it is no good to leave fire safety, for instance, to a single professional adviser or some security guard, and it is not enough to let safety supervision be handled by foremen who have already enough on their plate and are bound to regard the checking of unobstructed escape routes as just an unnecessary, extra chore. Safety should be an attitude, it should come readily to everyone but, as a spokesman put it, 'those who organize and teach safety must be of top quality: it can be more dangerous to be half-trained by an inferior man than not at all'.

In a submission to the Robens Committee on safety, the TUC emphasized that in the 1960s (when labour problems and strikes were as much in the news as today) on average seven working days were lost due to accidents and injuries for each single day lost in industrial disputes. The unions saw the rising toll of industrial accidents as a major national problem and demanded that it should be tackled on a national basis because, unlike some government departments, they believed that 'the great majority of accidents can be prevented'.

But to get real results, the spokesman added, 'management, too, must be properly trained. There are courses run by local safety groups, by the British Safety Council, RoSPA – yet how many board members go along to learn about fire, its prevention and the ways of fighting an outbreak? I was once lectured that "With any intelligence you don't need fire-prevention training – one just doesn't throw away burning matches, and that's that." This was a managing director.'

A technical expert, who now tests fire extinguishers for a research establishment, commented:

The trouble with intelligence, logic and clear thinking is that they may lull the thinker into a false sense of security. For one thing, when you face an emergency, you may not have the time or the nerve to think it all out for yourself. Another problem is that you may not be able to virtually invent, single-handedly, there and then what people have accumulated in knowledge and experience over the centuries. And finally, at some stage, especially if you were successful up to a point, you may feel so pleased with yourself that you just stop thinking. That is when your achievement may become the cause of another disaster. I should know. It almost happened to me.

I was seventeen years old, and never had any training for fire-fighting. We never even had fire drills in those days. At the place where I worked as an engineering apprentice, some rubber solution caught fire on the first floor. As I looked at the flames, a picture appeared to me quite clearly: an extinguisher. I didn't quite know where it was, but the picture was so precise that I ran out and down the stairs and found it without any difficulty. Racing back to the fire, I just quickly glanced at the instructions, understood it almost instinctively, and used the extinguisher the right way and most effectively. The fire was out within seconds and everybody was very pleased with me. You can imagine how pleased I was with myself.

There was some cheering, and on a wave of glory, I returned to the ground floor . . . and proudly replaced the virtually empty extinguisher in its brackets on the wall. Luckily, my boss spotted the mistake, or else somebody would have been in for a bit of a surprise at the next fire.

A major training problem is caused by the fact that people like to ridicule repetitions as something totally superfluous: 'All right, the pattern has been established, there are fire notices all over the place, everybody has been told how to raise the alarm, notify the switchboard or what, everybody has been told what to do when the alarm is sounded, everybody has seen the route to follow out of the building and everybody knows where to present himself for a roll call after escape – so what else is there to be said?' This can be heard over and over again, because most of us refuse to believe that in a true emergency, when sometimes we must act against our natural instinct, we can rely only on regular drills that have established a *second nature* to save lives.

Even in the building which houses the headquarters of the London Fire Brigade Fire Prevention Branch, where one would expect a natural and exceptionally intense awareness towards the fire risk, people seem to behave like others everywhere else. Robert Peskett said:

When the fire alarm is sounded, people here react very swiftly. They never know whether it's a practice run or if it's for real. They commence evacuation in an orderly fashion – and loads of them proceed to the lifts! (None, I hasten to add, is one of my officers.) It's about the worst they can do. We keep teaching and drilling people not to do it. Yet instinctively, they turn towards the means of exit they use every day. Even if they know the emergency route perfectly well. When we ask them why they do it – there's hardly ever an answer. Or they say 'it's stupid, really, I wouldn't know why I went that way'. Haven't they read the fire notices? 'What notices?' We have the instructions clearly displayed on boards throughout the building. But people's eyes get used to them. They pass them every day, on their way in and out, they don't notice them any more.

Mike Doherty explained:

This instinctive use of the lifts is always dangerous because the fire might burn out electrical installations before people reach the ground floor. If this instinct is coupled together with wrong fire drill instructions, disaster is immediately on the cards. In a small, two-storey warehouse it has just cost us two lives. When we got there, it was discovered that two people had been trapped in the goods lift between two floors. There was no escape hatch on top of the cage, and that shaft was a real inferno. While our men fought for those two, for three hours in tremendously punishing conditions, we discovered how stupidly wasted those lives were. Fire instructions had, in fact, encouraged staff to use the lift for evacuation. Yet another part of the drill made it the duty of a responsible member of the management to shut off all power supply as soon as the alarm was sounded. When we got there, we restored the power, of course, but it was too late. The wires had been burnt. We had to break into the shaft, and fight, risking men's lives – for two corpses.

In 1972 a study of people's behaviour in fires* indicated that the first action taken in an emergency was influenced by training mainly in two respects: raising the alarm and organizing

*Peter G. Wood, Loughborough University of Technology.

evacuation. Even if one accepts that fire drills achieve something truly noticeable only in these areas, there can be no doubt about the value of training. This is why fire officers can be absolutely infuriated when they visit hospitals, for instance, only to find that out of several hundred employees, a cook, a couple of cleaners, a student nurse and perhaps a clerk are all who will spare the time to attend the lecture.

Fire-prevention officers complained: 'We are not there to teach them. We're only supposed to supervise the drill, make sure that everything runs smoothly, and that everybody is getting the right instructions. Instead, we are often told off by the matron – with whom not even the doctors or the hospital secretary dare to argue – that due to shortage of staff and excessive workloads, we must "do what you can" with those who are available.'

And a Middlesex officer added:

Hospitals complain that in addition to staff shortage, they must deal with another difficult problem – the question of training staff who do not speak the language or if they do, their English may not be good enough to understand what is required from them in an emergency. But surely, if they can deal with a medical emergency, somehow they can be taught about raising the alarm and the evacuation procedure. They could easily do what the bigger, more responsible hotels do: issue fire notices in foreign languages, and even organize training in some of the more important foreign languages by getting their staffs together for a session.

The policy followed and the directives issued by the Department of Health are sound and quite clear. Not only must there be fire notices everywhere, but the Hospital Technical Memorandum No. 16 makes it a *duty* of all staff to study these notices, to know what to do in case of fire and how to use basic firefighting appliances, to be familiar with escape routes and help to 'ensure that staircases, landings and other escape routes are kept clear from obstruction at all times'. In this respect they were ahead of industry: they intended management and staff to *share* responsibilities even before the recent legislation. But the problem is enforcement. Individual hospitals are too powerful. Our only hope is that now, more and better fire officers *within* the health service will have the authority to strengthen defences.

The best example are the private hospitals: they cherish their licence, feel more vulnerable, and so they take greater care to carry out instructions to the letter. I have just had a case at such a hospital in the neighbourhood. They have a geriatric ward, handle many drug-addicts, and have plenty of the mentally unstable types of patients on their hands. But none of their staff is ever permitted to miss the twice yearly drill which we only supervise. Now that they had a fire which, in fact, could have been a rather serious one, they raised the alarm at once, we were there within a couple of minutes, and yet their well-planned evacuation of *all* patients was virtually complete when we arrived.

Apart from general criticisms regarding fire protection problems and the level of staff training in hospitals, fire prevention officers raised a very valid point: doctors show no interest in the fire problem which they tend to leave haughtily to nurses; student nurses are supposed to receive at least one lecture on fire precautions, and the use of firefighting equipment is demonstrated to them, but in their entire curriculum, fire is the only subject which is not part of their final examination. The result is a marked lack of attendance and attention. Many nurses may obtain excellent qualifications and serve in several hospitals for years and years without ever hearing a fire lecture, and it may happen by some not even exceptional coincidence, that they never participate in a single fire and evacuation drill. (The already mentioned Shelton Hospital fire in Shrewsbury provided a perfect, horrific example, of how it could happen resulting in twenty-four deaths despite some nurses' individual heroism.)

This important point ought to be pursued far beyond hospitals and nurse training. At London Transport, for instance, all new men in engineering had been given some training in fire prevention long before legislation made this compulsory. But not even apprentices were required to give some account of their preparedness. Bus drivers and conductors must take a full, quite extensive training course. Within this, they hear a single one-hour lecture on fire precaution and see a brief demonstration of the use of the type of extinguisher which must be carried on all public-service vehicles. But nobody knows exactly how much they benefit from this lecture: fire is not an examination subject. And the situation is the same all the way down to schools where children are now taught kerb-drill to achieve proficiency as pedestrians, but the devotion of visiting firemen rarely receives due weight and backing from the academic staff. ('Nice to have them around,' a headmaster once said. 'But policemen are better: they let the children play with their helmets.')

The result of unpreparedness can be seen in numerous outbreaks of panic and the wrong kind of actions in an emergency – both of which increase the gravity of a potential disaster. The above-quoted Loughborough study found that, irrespective of several factors (time, age, presence of smoke), 'the proportion of people who had never received training is significantly greater in casualty-producing incidents'. It may be due partly to the lack of training and partly to laymen's inability to assess the threat in a fire situation that a remarkably high proportion of people are prepared to fight a blaze virtually with their bare hands.

This goodwill and readiness to 'have a go' against all odds – is it community spirit? instinct of self-defence? instinct to *do* something, anything, positive? – are the qualities which ought to be harnessed by training, because at the moment we seem to expect people to take a driving test purely from reading the manual – and even that only in the last few moments before starting the car.

Apart from throwing a bucket of water (an apparently simple but potentially dangerous act in itself if, for instance, burning fat, petrol or live electrical installation is the target), most people involved in fires, except those in private dwellings, have the opportunity to take advantage of the first one or two minutes, when it is still only a 'little fire', by using a hose-reel or a fire extinguisher. And most people are convinced that this is no problem at all, 'any idiot can do it, all you have to do is to read the instructions'.

But is it really all that obvious? Are the nurses (or the health authorities) such hopeless simpletons that they need (or need to issue) standard fire instruction notices like this: '. . . 4. Extinguishers. Take extinguishers to the scene of the fire, then – NOT BEFORE – operate' the equipment.*

'No matter what it may sound like, this instruction is not all that idiotic,' said Hamish Webster, Chief Engineer of Nu-Swift International. 'When people are panicky, they do all sorts of crazy things. We hear quite frequently that they pick up extinguishers and discharge them without going anywhere near the flames. It's just a waste. It deprives others of the opportunity of using them correctly.'

And this is not the only common mistake: people appear to be most inventive when it comes to wasting extinguishers as well as good opportunities in an emergency. A common folly is to throw the extinguisher into the fire, hoping for the best. This is frequently done even by security guards and night watchmen who are supposed to know better. A fire-prevention officer has recently come across a quite incredible case of uniquely efficient collective blunder: while waiting for the arrival of the fire brigade, a guard with obvious qualities of leadership organized several workers into a chain to pass along fire extinguishers to him so that, standing near the seat of the fire, he could throw them into the flames one by one. He later complained bitterly to the firemen that 'the extinguishers not only failed to put out the fire, they even failed to go off!'

Another regular problem is that untrained people use the wrong extinguisher for a given type of fire – or use it in a dangerous manner, splashing burning oil all over the place, in fish-and-chip shops for instance.

A study of *The Use of Fire Extinguishers in Dwellings*†

*Hospital Technical Memorandum No. 16.

†By G. Ramachandran, P. Nash and S. P. Benson, FRN 915, Fire Research Station, 1972.

demonstrated that in the few households where an extinguisher was available, it was almost everybody's first choice to attack a fire. Yet on the whole, in private homes, extinguishers were found to be only about half as effective as 'sundry means' (including buckets, smothering, garden hose, etc.). This was probably due to the complete lack of training, and the distant location of the equipment. Carbon dioxide and dry powder extinguishers were an exception, proving themselves as effective as any other means even in the hands of such newcomers to firefighting. (The result perhaps indicated the particular usefulness and efficiency of the modern multipurpose powders which are suitable for fighting the common domestic mixed risks.)

Fire prevention and firefighting experts hope that once training at places of work becomes truly routine everywhere (they particularly urge the fire education of painters, decorators, maintenance workers, handymen and those who do any welding or burning off), the right techniques and basic expertise will spread rapidly throughout the entire population.

The result of even minimal training has been demonstrated in numerous experiments. Fire officers believe that workmen can easily be trained to achieve quite considerable efficiency in a half an hour of dummy runs with an empty extinguisher – as long as they have the opportunity to actually handle extinguishers. For the less technically minded, it is far better to have an opportunity to discharge the firefighting agent. This is easy with certain types where the discharge can be interrupted at any point – and then several people can get the feel of it at the cost of a single re-fill – while with some others, a good opportunity arises with the legally required regular testing and discharge. (According to some specialists, women who use an extinguisher in the correct manner for the first time may be so shaken by the force of the discharge itself that they throw away the perfectly operating equipment, scream and run for dear life, creating panic in place of a golden opportunity.)

It has been recognized that both men and women fighting a

fire for the first time, find 'difficulty in handling the equipment properly, but after a while – say five to ten practices – substantial advances in fire control invariably result'.* American and British fire research establishments agree that a reasonably skilled (non-professional) operator can put out flames in an at least three times bigger area than a novice, irrespective of conditions (e.g. wind). And the difference was shown to be just as great when a manufacturer experimented even on dangerous petrol spill fires with experienced and inexperienced firefighters.†

Being untrained not only implies the lack of actual firefighting practice, but also, in most cases, such a total lack of interest that people who pass every day or work right next to or even own, privately in their homes, a fire extinguisher, never bother to look at it and read the instructions.

It has often been claimed that the instructions are so simple that you can leave reading them until the last minute – when the equipment is needed in an emergency. Even if one disregards the disadvantages a panicky, fire-threatened reader would have to face, the instructions may not be as easily digestible by all as some manufacturers seem to hope and believe, and the format ought to remain the subject of a serious study. Even a few casual and superficial questions put to haphazardly chosen laymen‡ revealed some disturbing trends.

One of these was that more than half of them, particularly women, were not quite sure what instructions like 'strike knob smartly' meant. They were not even sure which the 'knob' was, particularly if there was a guard. Instructions to 'remove guard' or 'clip' seemed to cause some confusion in many cases, with almost a quarter of those asked attempting to unscrew the entire head – a potentially injurious explosion hazard with

*P. Nash, op. cit.

†*The Nu-Swift Book of Knowledge*, op. cit., 1974.

‡Having left out self-confessed skilled or semi-skilled firefighters – those who said they had read and remembered the instructions were regarded as semi-skilled – this author asked forty-seven people between the ages of eighteen and sixty-three, in hotels, public transport vehicles, etc.

certain extinguishers. When a 'nozzle-cap' was meant to be struck on a hard surface, it seemed that in actual usage people would have been too gentle with it fearing, like with a bottle of much-shaken champagne, too early release in an unwanted direction.

When *Which?* magazine carried out tests, many similar mistakes were recorded* and fire brigades have a wealth of stories both about common and unusual errors. Some people simply refuse to believe that certain extinguishers have to be turned upside down to make them work, while others do 'strike hard' indeed: doing their best to knock off guard, knob and all – sideways.

Most of the better extinguishers give some illustrations as well as written instructions to help overcome language problems and the built-in resistance of some people to read, and let sink in, anything even vaguely technical. But on some extinguishers the instructions are faded, or obliterated in certain other ways; on one or two types the instructions are virtually unreadable in broad daylight when brand new; and on some types the instructions appear in a form that would present only hieroglyphics under emergency lights shining through smoke. And all this without mentioning people who have to find their glasses first before trying to acquaint themselves with the instructions.

The result is, of course, that firemen hear the complaints again and again: 'The wretched thing just wouldn't work' or 'all I got out of it was hissing air' because they wrongly did or did not turn 'the wretched thing' upside down.

The instructions on some extinguishers appeared to be outright dangerous for the uninitiated. They did not specify clearly – or it was quite time-consuming to discover – what type of fire the equipment was intended for. (It could be dangerous to use a strong water jet on a burning fat pan.) At least one type caused unnecessary delay and hesitation by instructing that it should be operated upside down and held 'perfectly straight'. (Would it injure the user if there was the slightest

*March 1967.

deviation from the true vertical?) And several others gave the general firefighting instruction: aim at the seat (base) of fire. (As *Which?* remarked: 'sound enough advice in most circumstances but not on curtains' where the top of the flames should be the target.)

Although the correct way of fighting fires with various types of extinguishers could be safely generalized, and the principles do not vary much within the appropriate range of risks for which a given type is suitable (see illustrated section, between pages 88 and 89), even the haphazard questioning of a few dozen people called attention to a peculiar problem which is usually ignored or completely overlooked. Those who at least casually read (let alone carried out in practical training) the instructions on a particular extinguisher, immediately had the fairly firm conviction that their newly gained knowledge would be applicable to any other extinguisher. Which is, of course, a major and most dangerous fallacy – best illustrated by the easy confusion over the right-way-up or upside-down operational types.

This being merely a matter of *standardization*, one would think that the problem could easily be solved once and for all. Unfortunately, it is far from the truth. For ridiculous as it may sound, it has taken many years of rather fruitless debates to achieve some hope for a certain degree of standardization.

In Britain 'just the extinguishers that use water come in some eight different shapes, four different sizes, and with seven or eight different methods of operation,' said Robert Peskett. 'Multiply the possible variants, and you get a huge number of possible combinations which then must be faced by each would-be user in a hurry. People find it hard to forget the idea of using extinguishers upside down because the old soda-acid is still very much with us, and it needs this juggling no matter how heavy the stuff is. You bang things to the floor, to the wall, this way, that way, even with a hammer – no wonder people choose to run for it.

'I believe that all types could now use a pistol grip and the trigger mechanism. I mean it's technically possible. But manufacturers stick to their own designs partly because they believe in them, partly because it would be more expensive to re-tool – at least with the new models they ought to have some standardization in mind – and partly because they hate any uniformity for marketing reasons.'

Hamish Webster agreed: 'Yes, technically, the trigger – or rather lever – system seems possible for all types. Its big advantage is that, virtually without any instruction, people understand a trigger: they squeeze it if they see one. In Germany they mostly use this type. In Britain, where the traditional techniques are different, fewer than half the types apply trigger mechanisms.'

In the same way there are great differences in preferences for extinguishing agents. In Britain it is still mostly the water and foam extinguisher – and about 90 per cent of them with the 'strike knob' principle, which has certain advantages, with a trigger to control the discharge. In other European countries there are few water types any more because powders have been accepted as the modern and effective agents. (In Belgium, for instance, virtually all extinguishers are the powder type.) The European argument is that portable equipment is basically for semi-amateur firefighters, and the most efficient agent, that can be used for numerous risk combinations, is supposed to give them the greatest assistance.

But while technical arguments about the comparative efficiency of various extinguishing agents and operational techniques may be understandable, it is difficult to see why there cannot be an agreement at least on colour coding.

America, Australia, South Africa, India, France, Germany and many other countries have already a national system – with some differences for which each fights as if the nation's future depended on it. Britain belongs to the small band of countries which could not establish a good national coding for easy recognition of the types of extinguishers for various risks. The reason may well be that some of the British designs are still the best and most popular in the world, and long-standing traditions die hard.

For some twelve years, a British Standards Institute Sub-committee tried to devise an identification standard. Pictorial and other symbols, brief descriptions and various coding systems were refused, and a colour code was found to be the best. To the user it would make no difference what extinguisher was marked by what colour, yet some countries, such as Germany and Austria, have always insisted that they must be red.

In November 1969 at last a draft for a British Standard was ready and sent to all interested parties. Comments were invited by not later than 29 December 1969. Although among dry powders there were very considerable differences (some are multi-purpose and good for wood fires, others are not), a compromise was reached and a colour coding was recommended for five groups of extinguishing agents: water, foam, dry powder (all classes), CO_2, and halogenated hydrocarbon.

Furthermore, it was recommended that the extinguisher should be marked to indicate the type/s of fire for which the extinguishing agent in the container was suitable. (See choice of extinguisher, next chapter.)

Comments were pouring in – and further discussions became necessary. Then more debates, and more attention to the international moves and developments expected in Europe. Five years later, in October 1974, the code was agreed on – except that a committee member raised just a minor additional point of no real importance, but it had to be sorted out and accepted by all members. This was expected to delay publication and formal acceptance by about another six months. At the time of this writing, the code is still in the pipeline. Which should give some indication of the problems to come on a world-wide scale of standardization regarding not only colours and operating mechanisms, but also the lowest common denominator for the instructions to users in a form that would overcome language barriers as well as those set up by illiteracy, the level of general education and practical traditions.

Meanwhile, those who learn to use an extinguisher must watch out for traps: not only in different buildings (place of

H

work, hotels, hospitals, etc.) and not only in different countries will they find different extinguishers (both in colour and system) to be used for the same class of fire, but they might also be misled within a single building where they might find old and new types or simply different types side by side, ready to confuse the innocent. But this, of course, could be a much lesser problem, minimized by specialists who, in the light of carefully weighed risks, would avoid dangerous equipment, choose the right types, find the right siting for them, and maintain them in perfect working order.

7
That Thin Red Line

When it is a time to fight – before it may become absolutely imperative to run – it is simply criminal to send people into battle with the wrong and inadequate weapons, and to expect them to hold up thrusting divisions of armour with the bent blade of a bayonet.

However crucial a role they may have to play in self-defence, fire extinguishers are no more than the first thin red line (or blue or black or cream or green) facing the enemy, and although due to tremendous technical advances, they may stem or at least delay the tide of flames, it is essential to recognize their limitations. The new British Standard definition duly emphasizes that they are *first-aid* firefighting appliances 'which can be carried or wheeled by hand and from which an extinguishing agent is expelled'. To give them a true fighting chance, it is vital to make the best choice of weapons.

It is also stressed by specialists that defences must be organized to ensure that if the first-aid weapons (including hand-pumps, hose-reels, buckets, sand, smothering blankets, etc.) cannot score an immediate, outright victory, their failure should not be disastrous in any sense. (The alarm has been sounded, evacuation has begun, help is on its way, the route of retreat is clear, etc.) The only exceptions are those most isolated spots where automatic, fixed installations are not practicable, help may not be available at all, and the opportunity to escape may be lost easily – aboard a boat at sea, for instance.*

*After accounts of 'the sheer horror and speed of a spreading fire aboard a small boat', and a report about an outbreak when several extinguishers failed to

Unfortunately, as a salesman put it:

Nobody, well, hardly anybody *buys* a fire extinguisher. Almost invariably, the extinguisher must be *sold*, somehow, to people who don't want it or don't know why they want it or don't know what they want and need. Oh, yes, perhaps the small, so-called extinguishers, the aerosols and the like, may be bought in search of a cheap Christmas present for Daddy. Otherwise, people remain frighteningly ignorant and gullible.

Today, when so many of us go to extreme lengths to study cars or carpets, to explore the market and to make the right choice before buying, even high-powered responsible executives can easily be conned and exploited by little fly-by-night 'makers' of extinguishers and their reps.

And a fire-prevention officer agreed:

There is nothing wrong with using a salesman's knowledge and practical experience as guidance – if he knows what he is talking about, and if he means to stay in the business so that he could be found and made to bear responsibility, at least moral responsibility, even several years later. But quite frequently we find that they're there to sell something, without delay and only once. They sell the wrong equipment for the risk, the type that may cause a great deal of damage if accidentally discharged – such as a water appliance in a computer room – or simply an unreliable, shoddy, sub-standard product that cannot do what it promises to.

For laymen, the choice is complicated by the peculiar situation that although extinguishers are meant to serve in emergencies and safeguard life and property, it is not even an offence to market any 'shoddy, substandard'† or outright

---

discharge, *Yachting Monthly* organized a test with extinguishers, some of them more than ten years old, sent in by boat owners. The good ones worked well even if they had been submerged in salt water for years. In its January 1972 issue the magazine reported its conclusion that on a boat, the extinguisher 'is the one piece of equipment over which money must not be spared; that merely to have the cheapest extinguisher on the market in order to comply with insurance requirements is not good enough.'

†See next chapter.

dangerous product. British (and other national) Standards exist and there are accepted basic requirements for testing. The Fire Offices' Committee, a body of technical experts working for the tariff fire insurance companies, examines all products and issues lists of the approved ones, but the lack of their approval is no obstacle to the success of an impressive looking cheap extinguisher – even if it is cheap in every sense.

Government authorities take the attitude that it is better to have *something* than nothing to fight a fire with. That the resulting false sense of security could be more hazardous than a total – albeit known – lack of equipment, does not seem to worry those authorities. And one should not even talk about 'the view of authorities' for no such unity of attitudes exists. Not only countries, but also local authorities and even individual fire chiefs, differ greatly concerning the levels of acceptability. Numerous British fire brigades still prefer the old cumbersome shaker types and believe that dry powder extinguishers are no more than toys, while many of their colleagues are greatly impressed by demonstrations and claim that 'multipurpose appliances go 80 per cent of the way towards the ideal answer to a layman's fire problem and first-aid needs' – a controversial position which does not help the person who must make the choice for a home, hotel, hospital, shop or factory.

The order of important factors is also hotly debated. The industry wants contents and construction specifications, while authorities would prefer performance minima whatever the extinguishing agent or the method of discharge. Some specialists put efficiency or reliability at the top of their lists, while Find Graucob, with a lifetime's experience in manufacturing extinguishers, insists on giving *safety* – i.e. the user's safety from explosion or harmful contents – the place of honour among requirements, to be followed by efficiency, reliability, portability, speed of operation, conformity with standards, speed of reloading, ease of maintenance and other vital elements . . . with the price only way down the list, for the cost of an extinguisher, in proportion to what it may have to defend, is almost negligible.

Once the risk – including the type of occupancy, sources of ignition, the menace of rapid spread and, above all, the type of materials likely to burn – at any given premises has been established, the choice of extinguishers must depend, in the first place, on matching the most suitable and practicable extinguishing agent against the hazard.*

Water Extinguishers
For Class A, wood, paper, textile and similar fires.

Fires in most ordinary solid combustible materials can be best extinguished by cooling action, and unless this is done effectively, re-ignition remains a constant hazard. Water is particularly suitable because it has the best cooling properties and it can penetrate most surfaces to reach deep-seated fires. Although a spray is best to cover a large area, the better types are fitted with nozzles that can provide a spray or jet (to reach inaccessible places) as required. For the same reason, the range of the equipment is also important.

It is dangerous to use water on flammable liquids because of splashing, on live electrical equipment and in the presence of electricity because water itself is a conductor.

'Wet water' (containing some detergent) can penetrate textiles more speedily than ordinary water, and its use is the latest technique to reach deep-seated fires in modern upholstery treated by a water-repellent agent.

Foam Extinguishers
For Class B, liquid fires.

The foam, a stable bubble-structure, excludes oxygen by forming a blanket over the surface of burning liquid. As it

---

*Classification of extinguishers according to Draft for British Standard. The four classes of fires/materials – A. B. C. D – are listed more fully on pp. 75-6.

remains in position for a fairly long time, the liquid can cool sufficiently to avoid re-ignition. This is a particularly important feature of outbreaks at premises where the heating or burning of a flammable liquid is a part of normal procedures.

On flowing liquids, and on some liquids with peculiar chemical properties, the formation of a foam blanket may be impossible. In such cases other extinguishing agents can be used. Like water, foam is a conductor and its use is dangerous where electricity is present.

Dry Powder Extinguishers
(1) BCE type for Class B (liquid) and Class C (gas) fires – also in the presence of live electrical equipment.

Dry powders (based mostly on sodium or potassium bicarbonate with additives) are generally ideal to cover large flame areas quickly, deal with free-flowing burning liquids and prevent spread to surrounding materials.

The secret of their effect is that they kill the flames by rapid chemical inhibition of the flame processes. Most powders have only a rather limited cooling capacity, and so users must reckon with the hazard of re-ignition, particularly if a heating process cannot be quickly stopped. Such extinguishers are sometimes only a temporary though effective solution – injured racing drivers have been freed and removed from burning wreckages under a cloud of powder. Powders are suitable for fires involving electrical equipment because they do not conduct electricity.

(2) ABCE (general or multipurpose) type for Classes A, B and C fires in the presence of live electrical equipment, with the exception of flammable metals and fires involving very high voltage installations.

An extinguisher being a first-aid weapon, intended mainly for the use of amateur firefighters, these multipurpose powders are – or at least will soon be – the true answer to the fire problem in modern conditions where electricity is almost always present, yet many official and specialist publications tend to ignore their existence. (The already quoted Hospital Technical Memorandum No. 16, for instance, deals at length with the old-fashioned, messy, hard-to-maintain soda-acid extinguishers, but does not even mention multipurpose dry powders.)

Multipurpose powders are based on ammonium phosphates or similar salts, with a variety of added ingredients which prevent caking and ensure free-flowing, reliable discharge.

(3) Special powders for Class D, metal fires.

These have been developed to deal with combustible metals because the other powders (BCE and ABCE) are not effective on Class D fires.

CO₂ Extinguishers
For Class B (liquid) and Class C (gas) fires and live electrical equipment.

Carbon dioxide has definite advantages over foam in dealing with liquid fires (speed of effective action, easy access to escaping burning liquids in any position), but as the gas, unlike the foam blanket, keeps moving away, the cooling effect is shorter. Its special value is that it leaves behind no contaminating deposits, and so it is particularly suitable for use on fires involving delicate machinery, and laboratory, electronic and kitchen equipment. (CO_2 does not conduct electricity.)

Halogenated Hydrocarbon Extinguishers
For Class B (liquid), Class C (gas) and electrical equipment fires.

Better known as 'vaporizing liquids', halogenated hydrocarbons contain chlorine, bromine or fluorine, and release acid gases as they decompose in a fire and subdue the flames. They

Break glass type fire alarm next to fire-prone kitchen and store. . . .

. . . except that in the case of fire, when people are escaping from inside, the open door hides and blocks the alarm point. *London Fire Brigade*

Just as well – somebody in this building has already grown tired of tests and frequent false alarms due to malfunction. *London Fire Brigade*

Mixed Risk Fire (Classes A and B) extinguished by 26 lb (12 kg) 'Multy-Purpose' Extinguisher

Containers of flammable liquid (paint, thinners solvents etc.) are stacked on pallets in many warehouses and factory yards. Only one leaking drum is needed to create a serious hazard, as simulated here

The leaking drum is on the top of three loaded pallets, adjoining a stack of sixteen empty ones. A hydrocarbon solvent leaks at a rate of one gallon (5 litres) a minute. After one minute . . . ignition from a lighted match

Forty-five seconds later the blaze has a good hold, and flames lick the other drums and nearby wooden cases. Water is not a suitable extinguishing agent on a flammable liquid fire; foam is not suitable on a *running* liquid fire; and the use of BCE powder is precluded by the presence of wooden pallets

After burning for one minute (the probable time for a nearby worker to notice the outbreak and obtain an extinguisher) the fire is attacked with a multi purpose dry powder extinguisher

Four seconds later: the powder discharge provides a heat shield against the massive pillar of flame

Eight seconds later: the fire fighter moves in to kill residual pockets of flame

Fifteen seconds later: to ensure complete extinction, powder is discharged over the whole structure

Twenty seconds later: fire out, though the extinguisher is not fully discharged. Note that flammable liquid is still escaping from the drum, and that wood has also been burning. *Nu-Swift International*

Man-made hazards

. . . by the cabin-hook enthusiast who wants to ensure the free flow of goods and flames and fresh air and fumes by keeping self-closing doors open. *London Fire Brigade*

. . . by the ingenious matchmaker who fastens fire doors with fire extinguishers. *London Fire Brigade*

. . . and by the wiring artist who offers a good bedding for sparks. *London Fire Brigade*

act very rapidly, but usually, the extinguishers contain only a relatively small quantity because all vaporizing liquids introduce a certain degree of additional risk: their released gases are toxic – with some intoxicating, anaesthetic or poisoning effect. Compared to the potential benefits this risk is small and acceptable, e.g. in CBM, BCF and BTM (positively dangerous in CTC – see next chapter – and methyl bromide, MB, never to be used in hand extinguishers), but because of the hazardous element, these extinguishers should not be kept or used in confined places.

Vaporizing liquids are best for small liquid fires in open air (or where thorough ventilation after use is possible), particularly to deal with petrol- or oil-driven engines, and can be quite effective against small incipient Class A fires, too; they are non-conductors of electricity and so can fight fires in electrical equipment but may create some corrosion problems.

Apart from the general principles and the aim of finding the best possible match for the likely risks, would-be lay buyers of extinguishers must bear in mind a number of other, vitally important points when selecting the right equipment. The *method of operation* is one of these. Whatever they choose – stored pressure or gas cartridge types* – the best is to have uniformity of operation throughout any building. Training of staff or members of the family is simpler in this way and the one system – e.g. all extinguishers to be used in an upright position – helps to avoid causing confusion in moments of emergency and panic. (The greatest still surviving fallacy is that 'all extinguishers must be turned upside down and banged on the floor'. Sometimes even young people who have never seen such equipment believe that. If in a newly equipped factory

---

*Stored pressure extinguishers – the vessel and the fire-fighting agent are under constant pressure, any deterioration is easily detectable, even by laymen, particularly if pressure gauge is fitted. The system ensures reliability and efficiency and in these respects, as well as in safety to the user, it is superior to those in which the piercing of a gas cartridge – liquid CO_2 or nitrogen – releases the expellant.

just one such ancient relic remains on the wall, it may cause potentially disastrous moments of hesitation when quick reactions are most needed.)

The *ease of operation* must be seriously considered. Stored pressure types are attractive in this respect, too. It is important that the locking device which prevents accidental discharge should be easily removable in a simple manner, and no juggling – such as inversion and vigorous shaking – should be necessary before actual operation.

Choosing extinguishers of the right *size and weight* may require a fine balancing act between the likely hazard (how big an outbreak would be? how much of the right extinguishing agent would be required to stand a good chance of success?) and the available personnel. If it is likely that only women or the elderly will be present when first-aid firefighting must be performed, it may be better to choose lighter types or two smaller rather than one large extinguisher of the required type.

People's training, preparedness and likely emotional reactions – including panic – are also a factor. (Some extinguishers may discharge all their contents in about eight seconds. They are all wasted if the operation begins out of range because there is no time to approach the fire or else if the operator must try to work out the best way of attack only during those precious seconds.)

The *mess and damage* an extinguisher may cause by accidental discharge or intentional operation must also be a basic consideration. Sometimes such destruction may be much greater than the actual loss caused by the fire. Water may ruin sensitive electronic equipment. Dry powder, although non-toxic and harmless in itself, may create a mess in a kitchen or at a stamp-dealer's. As it emits a huge cloud behind which the firefighter can approach the flames – or retreat in safety if necessary – it may obscure vision and make escapers lose their way.

The old-fashioned, virtually obsolescent, yet still available soda-acid extinguisher is the biggest mess-producer of them all. (Perhaps the only one to beat it in this respect was the old chemical foam machine – some of the type require eleven operations to activate them.) It contains water with a sodium bicarbonate solution and a glass bottle of sulphuric acid. When it is operated, the bottle is punctured, the acid is released to react with the alkaline solution and expel the water. The presence of acid is an additional hazard associated with this type: such extinguishers had to be banned in prisons because the inmates frequently pinched the bottled acid to wield it as a most dangerous weapon.

Most other types can also cause a mess if discharged or stored in the wrong position. In schools, children used to give a bang to the old cone-shaped extinguishers – and fun it was, too, to watch everything in range being damaged irrevocably unless clothes and books and equipment could all be soaked and washed thoroughly without delay. When a foam extinguisher was pushed off its wall-bracket and activated accidentally, it destroyed much of the stocks in the hygienic store of a medical supplier.

Choosing an extinguisher for a *private home* is not a very simple question. The decision must be influenced by numerous factors – not the least by the price-tag attached.

Because of the multiplicity of hazards, ignition sources and fuel (all the materials likely to be ignited in a fire), it is generally accepted that a multipurpose dry powder extinguisher is probably the best compromise. The American National Fire Protection Association (NFPA) advises that a stored pressure water extinguisher would be a good second choice in addition to the multipurpose one. Chris Reynolds, Chief Chemist of a leading manufacturer, has however, some reservations about this:

I have a water and a BCF extinguisher in my home, and my wife and I know how to use them. But the mere presence of more than one appliance may cause some delay in firefighting through hesitation in picking The Right One for the purpose. Take water, for instance. It's most people's first thought as a firefighting agent, it's extremely effective, too, but people are usually advised not to use it in the presence of electricity. I know fire brigades often advocate the old bucket because they feel that all one has to do is to switch off the power supply and immediately we have an ordinary, non-electric fire. Which is fine when there is an expert firefighter on hand – but do amateurs have the time and presence of mind to go and switch off the power, then return to the fire and start putting it out? Besides, experienced firefighters would just go ahead and use a bucket or a water extinguisher quite merrily if the electrical equipment involved in the fire was below 250 V. But can the average user of first-aid equipment afford the luxury of thinking it all out in a cool and collected manner?

This kind of reasoning was strongly supported by some findings of a Fire Prevention Campaign survey in 1971. Six per cent of the householders questioned claimed to own an extinguisher, and almost half of these stated that theirs contained foam – both unsuitable for general use and relatively expensive. It was suggested that people probably had no idea what they kept in their homes for their protection (a sad comment on fire education), but it also seemed possible that in that particular area (Tyne–Tees), at the time, a somewhat ruthless organization's door-to-door salesmen sold successfully what they stocked rather than what their customers really needed.*

Extinguishers ought to play a much greater part in fighting fires *in road vehicles* than they have done up to now.

The annual number of fires on the road is approaching the twenty thousand mark, and more than half of these involve private cars. Some outbreaks are due to crashes, but most of them are caused by common electrical or engine faults. The suddenness and extent of destruction usually surprises drivers. While, logically, one would expect no great difficulty in escaping

---

*General merchants who stock and sell extinguishers often regard the range of available types as something to satisfy the individual customer's whim. A rather large order from Mauritius – shown to this author as an example by an international manufacturer – revealed that the dealer wanted to have a bit of everything, regardless of the likely needs to arise in his particular, non-industrial area, and in total ignorance of re-filling, re-charging requirements to back up his sales.

from burning vehicles, some five dozen people are killed by the fumes and burn injuries. Lorries have a particularly bad record on motorways where they tend to travel faster than is good for them. (Some 40 per cent of the lorry fires on motorways are attributed to the speed-induced increased risk of tyre or frictional heat.) Public transport vehicles – including London cabs – must carry extinguishers . . . and not without good reason: each year some six hundred buses, coaches and mini-buses catch fire causing injuries as well as some fatalities.

Unfortunately, there seems to be a great deal of uncertainty and disagreement concerning the most suitable type of extinguisher for road vehicles. Some specialists like to point out that according to the available statistical evidence, 'water from buckets' has a higher firefighting success rate than extinguishers can claim. In this respect, however, statistics are a completely *l'art pour l'art* exercise: how frequently are buckets of water readily available on the open road, particularly on motorways?

Other specialists are still prepared to defend that highly dangerous, toxic firefighting agent: CTC. They say that it is harmless on the road in the open air. They also claim that it is most effective because while CTC was carried by all buses and coaches, this then standard agent put out the highest number of fires successfully before the arrival of the fire brigade. Both arguments are dangerous and totally misleading. The first because fire brigades can recall quite frightening cases: a motorist, not seriously injured but trapped in his burning car, was killed by a benevolent lorry driver who sprayed him and the fire (effectively) with CTC. In another case, a minor upholstery fire was dealt with successfully by the driver himself on the hard shoulder of a motorway. Soon after restarting, the car careered across the central dividing line – as if out of control. The occupants were lucky: they survived the crash. There was nothing found in the car or the driver to explain the sudden odd behaviour, but fire officers suspected that some CTC remained in the car and had a mild intoxicating effect on the driver.

Against the other argument, a study of 562 bus cases in 1969*
gave conclusive evidence. True, the greatest number of fires was
successfully extinguished by CTC, but this agent was applied,
mostly in vain, in exactly twelve times more cases than foam,
its nearest rival. A proportional examination reveals, however,
the true success rate. CTC succeeded in two out of every eight
cases; foam and buckets of water achieved a ratio of two to six;
water, soda-acid and gas expulsion extinguishers won two
battles out of every five; and dry powder turned out to be an
easy winner with success on two occasions out of every three
attempts.

Against dry powder, fire prevention experts offered only one
warning: accidental discharge may occur in a car or bus-driver's
cabin where a large volume of powder could suddenly obscure
vision. Accidental discharge is, of course, a slight hazard with
every extinguisher and, unfortunately, it is no solution to keep
it away from the driver by storing it outside the compartment.
In the boot – access would be greatly delayed. Under the
bonnet – it can cause more damage than not having it at all!
For any outbreak is most likely to begin just there. If the
driver opens the bonnet to investigate the source of heat and
smoke – and to get to the extinguisher – the bonnet will direct
any flames underneath right into his face.

Whatever type is required for any purpose in any position,
the *simplicity of maintenance* could – and should – often be the
final, decisive factor in choosing extinguishers. For with some
types, maintenance can be a costly and troublesome affair even
though regular testing and inspection according to the manufacturers' instructions are not merely a matter of compliance with
the law – these are to ensure the reliability and constant readiness of the equipment. (Extinguishers which need regular discharging, recharging and much expert attention are, therefore,
at an obvious disadvantage. A checking and servicing contract
with the makers or suppliers may work out to be relatively

*I. B. O'Hara and S. A. Lewis: *Fires in Buses, Coaches and Mini-Buses*, FR
Note 936, Fire Research Station, 1972.

cheap – and give peace of mind – if a fair number of extinguishers need to be looked after in, say, industrial premises, particularly where no full-time fire officer is employed. But even in factories – not to mention smaller workshops or private dwellings – equipment with a pressure gauge is the easiest and cheapest to check by just a glance at it now and then.)*

Fire brigade inspectors still find many old soda-acid or mechanical foam machines which were fixed to newly-built walls several decades ago – and have never been removed or checked over since.

A fire prevention officer said:

When we want to try one of these extinguishers, we just cannot get them off the wall without damaging them. Such neglect is now illegal, of course, but people do not see much more than a mere formality in our requirements. They seriously argue that if they never had a fire in thirty years, it's unlikely that they would start having any from now on.

When it does happen that extinguishers remain in their brackets until the wall itself comes down, there may be another risk. The demolition men, making room for a new building, like to salvage anything of value – and the old extinguisher is often just the bonus they are looking for. The sharks who buy these for a few pence are in the so-called second-hand business. They 're-condition' the old wreck – I mean re-spray it nice and red – and create an entirely new hazard for the unsuspecting buyer who likes to get a bargain . . . even if it may be virtually a time-bomb obtained so 'cheaply' from an unscrupulous merchant of death.

*The Fire Protection Association has a simple basic guide to choosing portable fire extinguishers: data sheet FS6001. Their FS6002 is a good summary of the siting, care and maintenance requirements.

8
A Cause for Alarm

25 July 1970 was a hot Saturday in Philadelphia, United States. The fireman on duty at the Gulf Oil Refinery received his routine instructions, which included 'the semi-annual inspection of extinguishers located in the area between No. 1231 and No. 1232 Still Cooling Towers'.

If he had ever had any doubts about the usefulness of this chore, irrefutable evidence awaited him outside the No. 3 Flood Control Pumphouse. A twenty-pound dry chemical extinguisher was badly corroded all over. As he lifted it down, the hanger bracket came with it, away from the wall. It was chewed thin by rust. He replaced the hanger bracket and the extinguisher by reserves, and returned the corroded equipment to the fire house where he would call the Foreman's attention to it first thing Monday morning.

Soon after 7.30 a.m. on 27 July, he showed the extinguisher to Richard Papit, the Fire Department Foreman, who instructed him: 'Take it out to the fire-drill grounds and use it for fire drill.' With that, unwittingly, Papit signed in effect somebody's death warrant.

After numerous devastating conflagrations and fatal disasters, oil companies have particularly good reasons to respect the fire menace. They have also learned to live with the risk. At this Gulf plant the semi-annual inspections were just one small part of the safety routine. Regular drill and practical instruction of the staff was another part of it. One morning each week the Fire Marshal of the refinery or his assistant, the Foreman, would take up to ten employees to the drill ground and teach them to use portable extinguishers on actual petrol fires: first a demonstration by the instructor, and then each employee getting a chance to have a go.

On Tuesday, 28 July, it was Foreman Papit's turn to teach six people. While he explained what he was about to do, some kerosene-gasoline mixture was dumped on the ground and a torch was prepared for ignition. A sudden gust blew the flame of the torch towards the mixture which burst into flames. The Foreman, unperturbed, picked up the first extinguisher. While all others watched the spectacle of the premature outbreak of fire, he pulled the ring pin which allowed him to depress a lever which would puncture a diaphragm on the carbon dioxide cartridge attached to the side of this particular type, and release the gas into the container. The cylinder would now be charged, the powder ready to be driven out by the pressure of 275 pounds per square inch (20 kg/cm^2), when the handle of the nozzle was squeezed. Except that on this occasion, there would be no time to give it the squeeze and let it all burst free the way it should.

There was an explosion. Nobody saw what happened. The trainees remembered the sound of a car backfiring. When they turned, Foreman Papit was on the ground, bleeding profusely. The ruptured cylinder had hit him in the face like a rocket, killed him instantly, and still had the power to propel itself onwards, through the air, on a some thirty-feet flight.

Without such tremendous, and even greater, pressure, the useful range of extinguishers would be reduced considerably, and great quantities of the firefighting agent would remain, wasted, in the cylinder. Although every extinguisher body produced by a reputable manufacturer is thoroughly pressure tested (with regular samples tested to destruction), corrosion in service can reduce the strength of the container so that the stored pressure type can lose its pressure whereas a cartridge type can rupture on operation when a higher pressure is released into a weakened container.

In a warehouse a carbon-dioxide extinguisher blew up while hanging on its bracket: it tore a hole in the wall. Another of

I

this kind, a fifteen-pounder (7 kg), exploded in similar circumstances, untouched on the wall of an auto body shop, five years and one month after its date of purchase. The top of the cylinder went through the roof and travelled an eighth of a mile; the bottom part tore through a car. (Eventually, traces of moisture were found in the cylinder: during inspections, the extinguisher had never been examined internally.)

In June 1972 a small fire broke out at Beechfield House, an old people's home in Lancashire. While the fire brigade was already on its way from nearby, the fiancé of the warden's daughter tried to use a two-gallon (9 l.) water extinguisher. As soon as the plunger released the CO_2 into the body, there was an explosion that burst the welding of the cylinder. The would-be firefighter was undeterred: he tried another two extinguishers of the same type – and both exploded in the same way. Luckily, nobody was injured. The County Council ordered stringent tests on extinguishers in all its establishments – including schools, clinics, mental homes and blocks of flats – because this most unusual mass-failure might have revealed serious deficiencies in thousands of similar equipment.

The *Guardian* (10 June 1972) quoted the owner of the company that serviced the extinguishers regularly: 'We service these extinguishers but you can't tell by looking at them if they are weak inside.' A fire prevention officer at Preston told the paper that an instrument with a mirror and light could, in fact, check internal rust. And the company concerned was a bona fide, responsible servicing specialist. Considering that, unlike this particular firm, many fly-by-night outfits only offer so-called service and the flimsiest pretence of checking and repairs, it seems almost a miracle that far more serious and fatal accidents don't happen. The question is: how long will our luck last?

The current level of safety is the success story of those who set the standards, of those who test every new design, and of the manufacturers who maintain meticulous care in accordance with their own undertaking '. . . that the above described extinguisher is identical with the prototype approved by the

Fire Offices' Committee; and that prior notice will be given in the event of any variation in design, construction or method of actuation from that of the prototype approved . . .'

And yet, despite all the care that goes into the design, construction and reliable performance of these devices, some failures occur. Long, troublefree shelf-life is an essential requirement, but there are tens of thousands around – purchased a long time ago – which used to be guaranteed for only three or four years. The authorities feel that owners, who bought them in good faith, cannot be penalized today by banning this virtually obsolete equipment 'in the light of new developments'.

Old soda-acid machines could cause an unexpected sudden spurt of acid, when the acid bottle is broken inside, because of the too close proximity of the charge to the nozzle. (The acid has burned many users and caused much damage even through sheer accidental discharge.) The old chemical foam extinguisher may take up to five minutes to generate full pressure – much too long a delay which often ruins the opportunity for successful first-aid firefighting.

Many extinguishers still in use have rather badly positioned carbon-dioxide cartridges which are not pierced properly when the machine is activated and this prevents effective action. The lingering memory of traditional upside-down-to-squirt soda-acid equipment still precludes occasionally the correct usage of some good powder extinguishers because when these are turned upside down, only the gas escapes, leaving the entire mass of firefighting agent inside the cylinder.

Yet the main problem is that the current state of the law permits the legitimate continuation of three rather dubious – or at least highly undesirable – practices: (a) the shoddy servicing of extinguishers (and other fire equipment) and the sale of substandard, so-called reconditioned models, by anybody who can get the business regardless of any qualifications; (b) the continued sale of CTC extinguishers, often as so-called reconditioned ones, by scrap dealers and fences; and (c) the free marketing of 'aerosols' – often described as the 'mini-menace'.

(a) In the United States strict regulations control servicing, but in Britain anybody can set himself up as a fire equipment service engineer: no licence and no proof of specialist knowledge or experience is necessary. In a way, such service amounts to falsifying the trade description of goods: if the service is not in accordance with the strict undertakings of the manufacturer, any BSI-approved equipment ought to lose its kite mark and the validity of the now only alleged FOC approval. An inexpertly serviced extinguisher may thus be used under false pretences to continue qualifying for insurance rebate which is granted when FOC-approved extinguishers are installed.

These changes are acceptable in law simply because the service and alterations are carried out, in effect, by the owner or for the owner – and not by the seller. Only the insurers could enforce more reliable servicing (e.g. by the manufacturer) if they stipulated this as a responsibility of the insured. (If somebody changed the engine of a car from a 1300 c.c. to a 2000 c.c. the insurers would want to know about it and would probably change the terms – or else the valid cover would be lost. In a way, the same could be done concerning fire equipment.)

Manufacturers cannot do much about this unsatisfactory state of affairs: the damage is suffered mainly by their customers, the owners of the equipment, who could indeed take action on discovering that their extinguishers were refilled, say, with the wrong kind of powder, but normally, they do not find out about the damage until the machine is needed – and then it is too late.

'It's not like a television set,' said David Wilkinson, a manufacturer's Research Manager. 'When your colour is wrong or the horizontal hold is gone, you call the TV engineer, and you can see it at once whether he's done a good job on it or not. With an extinguisher, you may not live to see the result of bad servicing which can ruin completely all the coordinated effort that has gone into the careful design and well-supervised production of a safe, reliable and efficient extinguisher.'

After years of consultation, a new, revised Code of Practice has been drafted. It prescribes what servicing should be done and how, warns about dangerous practices, and so promotes high standards. Adherence to this Code is still voluntary – it has no statutory force. The full benefit of such voluntary systems depends on public demand and – as in the case of the travel agents' organization – a strong trade association. Although this would offer certain advantages – the fewer laws and the less bureaucracy the better – there is some doubt about its effectiveness.

In many respects, it is still true that anything that happens in the United States today is likely to happen elsewhere tomorrow. American legislation was, in fact, introduced in the 1960s and although it certainly created law-breakers and illegal practices, it helped to improve the general standard considerably.

And there was plenty of room for improvement. J. A. Proven, Executive Secretary of the Fire Equipment Manufacturers' Association, gave the following four reasons for the introduction of the new law:*

'(1) the widespread presence of dangerous extinguishers that should be removed from service; (2) the widespread unintentional poor servicing being done because of lack of knowledge or control; (3) the considerable racketeering or intentional poor servicing; and (4) the need for a vigorous campaign to remove untested and substandard extinguishers from service.'

When the so-called servicing outfits were investigated, it was found that extinguishers with damaged shells, external and internal corrosion, overcharged and undercharged, and filled with improper firefighting agents, had all been passed as 'satisfactory' and labelled 'serviced'. Frequently, service meant a quick glance at 'the general condition' of the equipment. Pressure testing of cylinders was not even heard of by many service engineers.

*'The Need for Legislation on Fire Extinguisher Servicing', an article in the *Fire Journal*, November 1967, based on an address given to the Fire Marshals Association of North America.

Older types require particularly great and regular attention. Yet in America, many cases were discovered like these: water in the acid, uncapped or faulty acid bottles, caking, defective hoses and gaskets, improper filling, moisture in cylinder, under- and overcharging, wrong valves, etc. in CO_2 extinguishers. It was quite usual to charge for work not done, for parts not replaced and for 'refill' even by the wrong agent – as in a British case, when two-gallon (9 l.) soda-acid extinguishers were refilled with foam compound.* (When this was queried, 'the works stated that these were the fire extinguisher refills they had in stock and they had, therefore, used them'.) A Chicago service company labelled a two-and-a-half-gallon foam unit as having been 'hydrotested at 300 psi' (21 kg/cm²). This despite the fact that a small hole in the shell had been plugged by a broken piece of pencil! Not only a 300 psi (21 kg/cm²) pressure, but even a light breeze would have ruptured it when activated.

Some of the examples reported by investigators revealed unashamed cheating on a vast scale. One case involved the 'servicing' of 524 extinguishers in a large Chicago housing project – with not one machine in good working order as the end result.

In Britain the servicing racket can be a similarly lucrative proposition, for the indication is clear: the people who do it certainly know the art of cutting costs as well as corners. In one case, affecting scores of extinguishers at a large industrial complex, the dry powder stored pressure extinguishers seemed to give a great deal of trouble: whenever the service engineers looked at them a great drop in pressure was reported in many extinguishers, and the subsequent invoice included items like 'repairs to eliminate leakage' and 'recharging' when, as it was discovered eventually, the extinguishers were in perfect working order throughout a period of some thirty months, and no repairs or servicing had been carried out.†

**Fire Protection Review*, August 1961.

†At the time of this writing, the case is still subject to litigation and therefore cannot be identified.

Cheap, often less than half-price, servicing can be undertaken only if every trick in the book is used.

Those servicing sharks never seem to notice on their 'inspection' rounds that some extinguishers may be erroneously positioned in locations where an industrial process, for instance, may produce high temperatures which can cause dangerous pressure building up inside firefighting equipment. In a stored pressure extinguisher the normal working pressure can be as high as 300 pounds per square inch (21 kg/cm²). The vessel itself is designed to a very considerable safety margin: it will only burst at pressures in excess of 1200 psi (84 kg/cm²).

To guard against this some stored pressure extinguishers are sealed by a special diaphragm which also acts as a bursting disc. This disc, which is only about two thousandths of an inch thick, performs a fine blancing act. It can withstand the working pressure without allowing any leakage, but when over-heating occurs, it bursts safely, at about 500 or 600 psi (35–42 kg/cm²) – long before the cylinder would fail – and lets the extinguisher vent itself.

In some instances the diaphragm is soldered into position. Where this is done it is vital that the correct type of solder and soldering techniques are used, otherwise the diaphragm will 'creep' under the constant pressure to which it is subjected in service, with eventual failure. The use of too much solder or too thick a diaphragm may deprive the extinguisher of all reliability by making it difficult or impossible to pierce the diaphragm when needed.

The racketeers do not bother to use the correct materials or manufacturing techniques. To them, the top of any old cocoa tin seems just as effective as the more expensive nickel disc – for the job of keeping the working pressure in. Perhaps it does not even occur to them that the tin is about four times thicker and stronger than the original part, that their newly applied sealing disc may withstand greater pressures than the welded body itself, and that it will not permit any safe 'letting off steam' – not until the whole extinguisher explodes . . . perhaps killing a fireman fighting the flames nearby.

And yet in Britain today such potential murderers are not breaking the law. They are entitled to carry on servicing fire equipment – and engineer 'totally fortuitous accidents'.

The most common servicing error by the ignorant, negligent or unscrupulous engineer occurs in the actual re-filling/re-charging process.

Good extinguishers are conceived as a single unit: the container, firefighting agent and pressure charge must match to ensure safety, long reliable shelf-life without the need of much maintenance, and smooth and rapid discharge whenever the time to use the device comes. This design for unity is disrupted by the use of the wrong kind of firefighting agent, for instance, when the racketeer or the do-it-yourself service department perhaps genuinely believes that one dry powder is just like another, and that they can be mixed or substituted for one another without any detrimental effect.

J. A. Proven said: 'There is a serious indifference about putting the wrong chemical in an extinguisher – one of the most dangerous things that can be done, particularly with the new 'multipurpose' dry chemicals. Mixing a multipurpose dry chemical with sodium bicarbonate-base or potassium bicarbonate-base dry chemicals can result in a build-up of pressure within the extinguisher that not only may ruin the efficiency of the extinguisher but certainly presents the danger of explosion.'

Chief Chemist Chris Reynolds explained:

When ammonium phosphates and similar salts (the base of multipurpose powders) are mixed with a bicarbonate in *perfectly* dry conditions, there may be no problem. But the presence of even the slightest trace of any moisture will inevitably start a chain reaction. The mixture begins to cake (as caking prevents discharge, this is a basic problem manufacturers must solve) and produces some water and carbon dioxide. The additional water increases the speed of reaction in the mixture and more CO_2 plus even more water is produced. If there is no venting, eventually the CO_2 pressure may build up enough to cause an explosion.

In the manufacture of extinguishers, tremendous care is taken to keep BC and multipurpose powders well apart from each other. (Our firm produces the different extinguishers and handles the different powders in considerable physical separation: in entirely different parts of the plant.) The production process is also devised to ensure that no moisture should be left in the vessel when it's sealed. This requires a full range of technical facilities – and decent servicing needs exactly the same facilities if refilling is to retain the standards of the original product. Unfortunately, the service racketeers often fail to clean the vessel completely before they refill a multipurpose extinguisher with, say, ordinary dry powder – and their technique is not noted for perfection in excluding moisture.

It is, of course, only a matter of 'minor oversight' that they fail to re-label the extinguisher and mark the change in the firefighting agent or even the name of the servicing outfit. This is not merely a fraudulent practice and a creation of outright danger to the user, but also a cause of mistakes in the application of the machine: if somebody believes that he has a multipurpose extinguisher, he may try to put out for example a Class A fire, without ever realising that he is using an ordinary BC powder – in vain, of course. The delay may result in anything from unnecessarily extensive damage to the loss of buildings or even lives.

(b) The trade in second-hand, so-called reconditioned extinguishers is also perfectly legitimate – even though the hazard is quite frightening.

Several scrap-dealers pick up their firefighting wares at demolition sites. That the extinguishers so purchased for a very nominal price are dented, corroded or damaged in any other way, does not seem to bother this trade. Some of the dealers find that 'reconditioning' is the most profitable, and this is not very surprising if one considers what such 'work' involves. Usually, the old vessel is simply resprayed red whatever the contents. This covers up rust at least for a while. No attempt is made to check the cylinder or indeed the serviceability of the apparatus. The extinguisher is then displayed in a scrap-yard – or sometimes even at market stalls – in the open, exposed to the weather, until sold to the ignorant, the bargain-hunter or anyone who believes that only the letter of the law need be complied with.

Occasionally, batches of extinguishers are picked up at auctions. When recently, a mill was closed down, 'lot 306' was sold for five pounds. Lot 306 consisted of twenty-one extinguishers, some of which were no more than the remains of empty, rusty shells. Yet none of these would be wasted in the hands of the truly ambitious 'reconditioners'. For many of them buy anything for cannibalization and a cheap supply of what they regard as spare parts.

This is how some machines were sold with syphon and discharge tubes blocked solid, others with soda-acid bottle cages tied together with string, or the wrong, entirely unsuitable, parts fitted to satisfy only the customer who wants to see that his new extinguisher has, say, a nozzle.

In some cases, where extinguishers had been weeping due to corrosion, the body was subjected to some cosmetic surgery under the soldering iron, and in an American case, the 'cylinder' was just a converted commercial carbon-dioxide container such as those used in vending machines.

Some dealers acted as common fences: they bought extinguishers from thieves who had stolen them from various buildings and public service vehicles. (A few years ago, vaporizing liquid extinguishers disappeared from London buses at such a fast rate, that a decision was made to paint these all black instead of the usual green to make them less attractive at least to the amateur thief and the vandals. That, of course, did not stop the professionals who had a safe and regular outlet for their loot.)

But the true boom in the second-hand trade began in the 1960s, when, following the example of numerous other countries, British authorities began discussions on banning the already mentioned CTC (carbon tetrachloride), a highly toxic fire-fighting agent, which was one of the most widely used vaporizing liquids but which could now be substituted quite easily by more modern, more effective and less harmful substances.

The debate on the subject has been hindered by the fact that many specialists believe, even today, that CTC is 'unpleasant' and 'irritating' or even 'undesirable' but not really harmful. The reason probably is that people's tolerance varies a great deal towards CTC. It is known that it can damage the liver permanently, but it is also claimed to be a mild sexual stimulant. A chemist administered quite considerable doses regularly to his lover – as an 'aid of sexual excitement' he said in a court case – without any harmful effect, yet damage was known to have been caused to others through the skin, by inhalation, and death by swallowing just a small quantity.

In a Canadian hospital a patient started a small fire with a cigarette. The staff quickly emptied two extinguishers on the fire – and killed the patient promptly. Both appliances were CTC-filled.

Robert Peskett, Assistant Chief Officer of the London Fire Brigade, used a CTC extinguisher as a young fireman: the fire was in a lift motor room, he only gave it a squirt of CTC – and found himself flat out after a few seconds . . . with a short hospitalization to give him time to think about it. Mike Doherty, his deputy, gained similar experience when serving in the Army fire brigade:

Two of us went to a boiler house fire. The door was closed, very properly, to contain the fire, and nobody was left inside. They told us what happened, but they forgot to mention one thing: they had already tried to put out the flames by the total discharge of two CTC extinguishers through the open door before failure persuaded them to 'lock the fire in'. As we entered, the asphyxiating effect hit us like a lightning bolt and respiration was cut off instantly. Luckily, we were pulled out quickly enough to get away without serious effects.

After an inquiry by the Central Fire Brigade Advisory Committee for England, Wales and Scotland, the Home Office recommended in 1970 that CTC and certain extinguishers containing toxic vaporizing liquids should be withdrawn from the market. The idea was to stop production and new sales within two years, discontinue the refilling of extinguishers with

CTC within five years, and allow only a short period of grace for those who already owned such apparatus.

All this was, however, only a recommendation, without any backing of legal enforcement. A new law perhaps did not seem necessary at the time because reputable manufacturers and dealers had agreed to accept the Home Office guidance. But the unscrupulous ones saw the makings of a true second-hand bonanza when the biggest users – such as government departments, schools, hospitals, local authorities, public transport companies, etc. – began to phase out CTC.

The fire brigades converted many of their CTC extinguishers to the use of BCF, a less toxic yet equally effective vaporizing liquid, but some machines were condemned and sold for scrapping. Although attempts were made to ensure that these machines were truly scrapped, there are good reasons to believe that these attempts were not entirely successful: many of the discarded cylinders were refilled with CTC and returned to the market as 'reconditioned' or sometimes 'new'.

The trade is even luckier with many other organizations which do not seem to take any serious precautions to prevent the renovation of their scrapped, obsolete extinguishers. Government departments, local councils and hospitals are selling their CTCs in bulk – and there is more to come up for sale because plenty of these dangerous extinguishers are still in various buildings awaiting their turn in the queue for 'planned obsolescence' and funds for replacements. The Hospital Technical Memorandum No. 16 still fails to say anything more positive than 'not recommended' about the 'very toxic' CTC. The Public Service Vehicles Regulations of 1972 allowed five years for the phasing out of CTC. The result is, for example, that at least a third of the London Transport buses are still equipped with CTC extinguishers.

The sharks' prosperity was further enhanced by the fact that the scrapping of thousands of extinguishers came hand in hand with the tightening of safety regulations in general and the stricter fire control of hotels and other premises in particular.

This meant not only that there was to be an increased demand, but also that there would be many new customers who had never needed and had hardly ever seen – let alone handled or tried to judge and choose – an extinguisher.

In 1974, when fire brigade inspectors were already busy enforcing the new regulations, inspecting thousands of premises and making their recommendations, bogus firemen began to visit particularly the smaller hotels, shops and various other firms to sell them good-as-new CTC extinguishers. These salesmen in uniform often claimed that the machines had special fire brigade approval: 'that's why they're marketed by ourselves, serving fire officers, to protect you and cut out the profiteering by the sharp operators who, as we well know, can be found everywhere these days'.

The fire brigades receive quite frequent information about 'small backstreet firms springing up everywhere to flog the old stuff' but they are powerless to do anything about it without the backing of the law. It appears that fire prevention officers will probably be able to object to the continued use of CTC machines on the basis of its unsuitability for hotels, for instance, but that will only mean that the poorest and most gullible customers will be the victims – the sharks do not bother to call again with the promised after-sale service.

Like bad servicing, the indiscriminate reconstruction of an extinguisher can ruin even the remaining efficiency of an old type. (There is a story circulating about the cannibalization specialist who once managed to build six new out of five old extinguishers.)

A particular problem in this respect is that extinguishers are not designed to protect the 'wide boys' and the do-it-yourself engineers against Murphy's Law: if it is mechanically possible to fit any part of any product the wrong way as well as the right way round, then someone, somewhere, some day will assemble it incorrectly.

Murphy's Law is completely international – it is the same expression in German, French, Arabic, Swedish and Japanese as well as in English on both sides of the Atlantic – but nobody seems to know its precise origin, although its chief victim is the aircraft industry which has been bedevilled by it since the days of Icarus. Americans believe that it is an Irishism. In Britain it is thought to be an Americanism. And nobody can find a trace of the unfortunate Murphy who gave the law his name.

Perhaps the best, the classic example of a killer valve was once researched and reported in full for the first time by this author.* The gist of the story was that a four-engined RAF transport aircraft crashed into a village in rather mysterious circumstances, killing most of its crew and passengers.

With the help of the survivors' evidence, from the examination of the wreckage and the aircraft service records, some peculiarities emerged: in the air, fuel was seen streaming from the No. 1 engine; afterwards, the gauges registered tremendous fuel losses within a few minutes; then two engines packed up in quick succession; a few days before the fatal flight the aircraft was serviced and a few minor repairs had to be carried out; then there was a test flight – uneventful – but with a strange entry in the log, unnoticed at the time: the aircraft had returned from the test flight with more fuel in one of its tanks than before take-off!

After these discoveries the main implements parts of fuel management in the air, cocks controlling the flow of fuel between tanks and engines, were examined and it was noticed that an arrow on a non-return valve pointed in the wrong direction. This reversal meant that instead of just feeding the engines, one tank was also over-filling another tank (hence the streaming over-flow), and when the first tank ran dry and the pilot tried to use the fuel from the second tank, the wrongly fitted non-return valve would not let a drop through – and the engines would be starved to death.

The ultimate cause of the accident was a plain design error according to the letter of Murphy's Law: the threaded portions

Aircrash Detective, Hamish Hamilton, London, 1970.

at both ends of the valve were identical! Although it had never happened in several years of service, it was just possible to overlook the arrow (which marked the correct direction of fuel flow through the valve) and fit the valve either way. Apart from the introduction of more rigorous control of servicing and testing, the threaded portions at both ends were redesigned to be different and prevent the repetition of the error.

Anti-Murphy design is now standard on all aircraft, but the devil is still occasionally irrepressible because even highly trained people can sometimes make quite incredible mistakes. Once a highly qualified aircraft engineer, for instance, simply sawed off an 'anti-interference pin' which prevented him from assembling an elevator part incorrectly, and the supervisors never checked his end-product because they just *knew*, beyond any shadow of doubt, that the part could not be assembled except in the right way.

The American Fire Equipment Manufacturers' Association has a record of many extinguisher malfunctions and failures due to the use of wrong substitute parts and incorrectly assembled parts. Anti-Murphy design for extinguishers is almost impossible because amateur servicing companies and backstreet second-hand traders are quite willing to resort to the use of just any replacements – e.g. the top of the infamous cocoa tin – and to turn one manufacturer's cannibalized product into spares for another make.

A technical expert who tests mostly new extinguisher designs said:

It is really odd how few, otherwise most reputable, factories can produce a decent, good quality weld. Sometimes the seam is just good enough to withstand routine test pressure. But when there is overcharging by inexperienced service engineers, Murphy's Law prevails: charge and weld are matched the wrong way.

Obviously, an extinguisher is an extremely simple piece of equipment compared with an aircraft, yet it's amazing how many things can go wrong. Parts fitted the wrong way may prevent total or even partial discharge, and I've just come across a real classic case: a rather tatty water extinguisher was fitted with a hose – a perfectly good hose – of another, much larger type. There was no clip to hold the hose in position on the side of the cylinder, so it was just hanging down to the ground.

It was brought to me for an expert opinion why the machine had failed when needed in an emergency. Unfortunately, it needed no expert to discover the cause: the nozzle at the end of the hose was blocked by dry mud.

I then learned what had happened. The apparatus had been purchased second-hand, as a reconditioned one. (The respray could hardly hide the corrosion underneath.) It was normally kept on a shelf, but a couple of months before the fire, it had been used for a 'dry-run' demonstration for staff in a waterlogged court-yard. Obviously, as it stood on the ground, the long hose permitted the freely dangling nozzle to sink into the mud. Perhaps somebody had even pulled it along with the nozzle scooping up more mud because the blockage was perfect.

(c) The third highly undesirable practice concerns the continued production of tiny toy-extinguishers – often described as the *mini-menace* – which have been exposed to numerous public outcries and protests, yet seem to be able to survive almost any storm.

The Director of the Consumer Council declared them plainly ineffective. A fire engineer was once quoted in a magazine saying that these were 'made for salesmen to sell and the public to buy, not for putting fires out'. They were sharply criticized for a great variety of reasons by Fire Chiefs and investigators of fires, by the British Standards Institution, the Fire Protection Association, the Fire Offices Committee, the British Safety Council, numerous independent experts, and specialists of the Joint Fire Research Organisation.

The length of the critics' list and the weight of these specialists are most impressive undoubtedly, yet the government remains unmoved and obstinately continues to permit production. The result is that each week door-to-door salesmen can peddle up to 30,000* of these symbols of false security. Housewives buy

*Safety & Rescue, a BSC Publication, February 1970.

them, motorists buy them, people on the look-out for cheap presents buy them – all customers hoping to get safety at a bargain rate. But what do they really buy? 'Trouble' was the laconic answer offered by most specialists consulted by this author.

From time to time, the campaign against the mini-menace is intensified on various levels. Gallant attempts are made to stir up the authorities' interest and prod them until some positive action is initiated. But so far, these attempts have been doomed to fail. The problem is similar to that of fire preventive measures: it is difficult to prove that Parliamentary time and a great deal of money were well spent because something did *not* happen as a result; it is equally difficult to prove with actual case-histories that lives might have been saved and less damage could have been caused and buildings might not have collapsed and cars might not have burned out if time had been not wasted on hopeless efforts to fight a fire with a toy.

In 1972, Leslie Huckfield, MP for Nuneaton, asked the Home Office to prohibit the doorstep sales of mini-extinguishers, at least to housewives: was it not scandalous 'that thousands of people were kidding themselves that their cars, caravans, boats and even houses were protected, when most of these things would not even put out a lighted match'. (Which requires a minor correction: most of 'these things' would put out a lighted match – just about – if and when they could be nursed to life and made to work at all.) The Under-Secretary of State at the Home Office refused to introduce legislation to ban their sale. He felt that most of the public had the common sense to realize that those things had only limited use. (The interpretation of the expression 'common sense' is fairly simple in such cases: if you agree with me you have it, if you do not, your common sense is lacking. In this case, the experts seem to have none of it.)

In some ways, the contents and shoddy workmanship of these extinguishers may represent an outright hazard to the user. Several of them are filled with peculiar mixtures of

K

vaporizing liquids which produce sickening, intolerable, toxic fumes even in the open air. In a confined space, these could knock out the firefighter. Others create such a large volume of dense black smoke that the user may lose his way out of a dangerous place.

The construction of the cans is also rather unsafe. The seal round the neck of the extinguisher is way below British Standards requirements. The cans must be mass-produced to keep the price down, and a high rate of failure is inevitable. (Such a high failure rate may be acceptable with other types of aerosols, such as hair-lacquer sprays, which are not meant to be available in emergencies.) When they are exposed to heat they may soon explode.

Very frequently, the manufacturers elevate the mini-menace to the state of some mighty panacea by making the wildest claims about its possible uses and applications. This in itself is a serious hazard, particularly when combined with false descriptions and inadequate instructions.

In America, hardware stores had great success for several years with various types of 'glass bulb grenades' which were only to be hurled into the fire to achieve amazing results – if the 'firefighter' was a top-flight fast bowler, one presumes. Luckily, this grenade has not yet invaded Britain, but there are plenty of others. Some of these are supposed to put out Classes A, B and C fires – which would truly be an incredible achievement if the Class A fire were bigger than the burning tip of a matchstick. As it is, the claim is just plain incredible.

Allegedly, others will not only fight various blazes, but will also keep away muggers, robbers and other attackers by a well-aimed squirt into the eyes of the assailant. (To some extent, this may even be true. Several mini-extinguishers are filled with a solvent which is also suitable for refrigerators as a cooling agent. It could therefore cool or temporarily freeze the eyes exposed to it, though the precise long-term effect is not predictable.) But this is also a hazard: as accidental discharge-prevention is not a standard feature of these designs, such extinguishers could also damage the defender's eyes – even if there is no attack by fire or muggers.

Safety and Rescue, a British Safety Council publication, had several of these mini-extinguishers tested, including one which was alleged to act as a pain reliever for scalds and burns, too. Although it was found that initially, on minor burns, the spray had the same soothing effect as cold water, 'it could be hazardous to use it to relieve pain at later stages'.

A further original and rather imaginative application of a product was suggested by its manufacturers: their particular mini could be used as an indoors air purifier.

Even if all the extravagant claims were fully justified, they would only add to the risk these freakish contraptions tend to create: as they are 'fun', proud owners like to show off with a squirt here and a squirt there; following the makers' advice, they might also purify the air, etc., with them; unwittingly, they would only empty the canister which then, facing a fire, would die with a pitiful sigh, because the firefighting contents is hardly more than a brief puff in most cases even to start with.

When various selections of mini-extinguishers were tested by fire brigades, individual experts for several organizations, the British Safety Council, magazines and newspapers (the *People,* for example), the Consumers Association and others, the total failure rate and general uselessness were found to be tremendous.

Amateur firefighters were unable to extinguish even small fires in most cases. Usually, the chief reason was that the equipment simply did not work. Some of the models needed two charges (the new, original, fully filled can plus another charge) to have any effect at all. When the *People* tested six models – all failed. When fire prevention officers of the London Fire Brigade tested some mini-models for the BBC, only one type produced any beneficial effect, and even in these expert hands, several failed to discharge any of their contents. (It is of no avail that some manufacturers urgently organize counter-demonstrations where their own handlers produce some good results: these demonstrations are never under professional test conditions, and what is more, if their own demonstrators could not produce *some* convincing achievements, the makers would only classify themselves as crooks who knowingly market useless products.)

A rather crucial 'test' was reported in 1971. When an invalid carriage burst into flames, the owner dragged himself free and tried to use an extinguisher issued to him by the Department of Health and Social Security. The equipment failed and the vehicle became a complete write-off. The same day, with remarkable efficiency, a replacement carriage was delivered to him. It came equipped with an extinguisher of the same type as the one that had failed. He asked the fire brigade to test it for him, and this was a most fortunate decision: for this extinguisher also failed to work.

It soon emerged that the makers guaranteed the type at the time for only three years, and recommended regular check-ups beyond that limit. The Department had ignored this advice and, even worse, continued supplying 'new' extinguishers which were already more than three years old at the time of issue. (The replacement received by the above invalid and tested by the fire brigade was already six years old.)

Following these dangerous failures, testing procedures were urgently introduced. The Department promised to withdraw all the obsolete equipment from invalid carriages. But while the manufacturer of the No. 1 and No. 2 failures (who had already warned other customers, too) devised a series of improvements to lengthen test-free shelf-life, the Department hurriedly issued yet another replacement extinguisher to the above unfortunate invalid: this time a small aerosol type!

(The invalid carriages purchased by the Department of Health after 1968 have all come complete with an aerosol type BCF extinguisher. As the vaporizing liquid content of this extinguisher is only 11¼ oz (320 g), it cannot qualify for BSI or FOC approval, but according to the ministry and the manufacturer, it complies with the Code of Practice established by the British Aerosol Manufacturers' Association, and it has been tested for an extinguishing capacity rating by the Joint Fire Research Station which 'accepted it for the purpose for which it is required'. When approved garages service these carriages, about three times a year, it is part of the regular schedule to check the serviceability of the extinguisher, too.)

If long, trouble-free and safe shelf-life is a key factor in the construction of a good extinguisher, most minis cannot even start in the race to qualify for FOC approval. Even worse: several of the makers fail to state a definite expiry date or may even give a false one.

The instructions for users are often muddled, incomplete or even dangerous. The usual claim that the extinguisher should be discharged towards the base of the fire is correct in most cases, but useless when tackling a curtain fire, for instance. Another unnecessary risk can be created by the absence of clear warnings what *not* to do with such extinguishers, and what fires must *not* be attacked with them.

In 1971 a Staffordshire housewife kept her cool when a panful of fat burst into flames. She went to fetch a small aerosol-type extinguisher, and tried to use it as told by her husband – who was selling such equipment. The result was that she suffered extensive burns on her neck and hands. Her husband asked the local fire brigade to investigate the accident. It was found that the firefighting agent in the extinguisher was CTC, and that the 'British Standard number' referred to on the container was applicable to condensed milk.

Strong objections can thus be made to even the best of the mini-extinguishers on several grounds:

(1) Lack of safety to user.

(2) Lack of reliability – due to cheapness being the main aim of design and production. They often fail.

(3) Inefficiency. Due to their size, even if filled with a truly effective firefighting agent and even if operating in a reasonably reliable way, they cannot hope to extinguish, at their best, in expert hands, more than the tiniest of fires. The discharge of the contents is usually so fast – no more than a few seconds –

that the inexperienced firefighters are likely to miss the flames altogether. To advise amateurs to approach the fire until they just cannot miss the flames would be highly irresponsible for they certainly cannot rely on such equipment to give them a fighting chance or even a safe retreat.

(4) Toy-like character: people are tempted to try them and show them to friends again and again, and particularly, if used for other ingenious purposes, too, the containers are likely to be empty by the time they are needed.

(5) False sense of security: even if owners of such equipment are unlikely to take extraordinary risks by feeling reassured about their firefighting readiness, the hopeless fighting attempts they may make in an emergency may cause dangerous delays in escaping, raising the alarm warning others and calling the professionals.

The Fire Protection Handbook of the American NFPA made this categorical statement: 'The public is best advised to purchase only those extinguishers which are listed or labeled by a nationally recognized testing laboratory.' This was because 'extinguishers are designed for emergency use to control and extinguish fires and should be thought of as vital tools to protect life and property'. Sound advice, undoubtedly, in the light of the fact that in several European countries, the United States and Australia, there are recognized grades on the basis of carefully evaluated extinguisher capabilities and limitations.

In Britain, however, no recognized testing methods and requirements, and no national standards have been established for the minis, which therefore do not break any law. British Standards cover and are applicable to only those extinguishers which contain certain minimum amounts of extinguishing agent, or which, in another proposed rating system, will extinguish a fire of a given minimum size.

Those who object to the introduction of a British Standard for the smaller extinguisher argue that the necessary miniaturization and cheapness of construction would make it impossible to talk about any acceptable standard, and above all, the problem is where to draw the line as the minimum requirement. They argue that 'if today one pound (0·45 kg) of powder or a pint (0·57 l.) of water were the lowest limit, tomorrow somebody would start the production of a micro-extinguisher with a thimbleful of something or other suitable for fires likely to be suffered by the Seven Dwarfs. Do we then devise a British Standard for that, too?

'Firefighting is not a game. There must be a dividing line between a toy and tool. Below that line there ought to be legislation to prohibit the manufacture and marketing of imitation extinguishers. In the absence of legislative safeguards for the public there is only one sensible course open to would-be buyers: seek out and listen to those who are qualified to give them advice. In most cases they will be warned against buying a mini-extinguisher. But there may be one or two exceptions: most reputable and truly professional manufacturers either stopped the mini-menace production altogether or developed and improved even their cheaper products to the point where these became virtually borderline cases . . . almost ready to comply with the British Standard requirements and pass the tests.'

It appears, nevertheless, that those whose duty it is to set the acceptable standards take an élitist attitude much too readily. For if there were approved standards for every size, even for the thimbleful to be used by the residents of a dolls' house, the law could enforce proper labelling according to the tests any extinguisher passed, and any safety-minded customer could see in comparable terms what he would be getting for his money. The aerosols in the invalid carriages are a good example: authorities should not be permitted to have it both ways. If that particular type is really good enough for those Department of Health issue vehicles, it should be good enough to gain British Standards and FOC approval so that other drivers, too, could buy it with confidence; or else, if technical experts have reason to doubt its efficiency or reliability, invalid drivers should be urgently warned.

New laws could put a sudden end to all the undesirable practices concerning extinguishers. Reluctant legislators, who are not yet ready to make a move, expect customers to be more discriminating in choosing. But is it not expecting a little too much from the public – the housewife, for instance – to learn all the tricks of the trade and challenge on firm grounds every statement of a fast-talking salesman of equipment or services?

Nomen est omen — but luckily, whatever the name, no one died in this bus when it burned out in a flash. *London Express*

All that water — and nothing to fight the flames with. Fortunately, at least the shore is near. *London Express*

Some of the small extinguishers for 'quick self-defence'. Will they offer even first-aid protection? *Camera Press*

The pictures on these two pages show the tragic sequence of events when a fire escape collapsed during a recent fire in Boston. *Opposite above*, the rescue attempt begins: the ladder moves into position. *Opposite below*, the fireman, standing with the victims, grabs the ladder as the metal structure gives way

Above, the woman tries to hold on to the fireman as the fire escape collapses, but fails. *Above right* and *below*, she and her two-year-old goddaughter plunge five storeys to the ground. She died but the child survived. *Associated Press*

Monsanto chemical plant, Texas — just a part of the fire that killed a town. *Keystone Press Agency*

The aftermath of fire: the remains of the Fairfield old folk's home — and of eighteen old folk. *Keystone Press Agency*

9
Momentary Indecision that Killed a Town

If one accepts the word and first-hand experience of a much-suffered fire victim that the mere discovery of a fire can make you 'the loneliest man in the world', then there is also ample evidence to support many sailors' view that a ship is about the loneliest *place* in the world when a fire is discovered aboard.

Fortunately, seafaring people are used to self-sufficiency, self-reliance in judging situations, and instant decision-making, yet it is too easy to err, through hesitation if nothing else. Almost three thousand ships have been lost at sea in the past decade. Many of these were small ones, coasters or fishing vessels with inadequate radio equipment, but in all, about three ships were lost in every four days – vanished in heavy seas, fell victims to storms, shifting cargoes, collision or fire.

One could list, repeat and summarize the crucial points that reveal the importance of preparedness for fire and re-emphasize how invaluable those first few moments of correct self-defence are, but nothing could tell all this better and give us all a stronger warning than a few case histories coming from those 'loneliest places'.

Thousands of small ship fires are never reported even though specialists have always recognized the fact that 'many major fires [aboard] are averted only by a narrow margin'.* The basic problems at sea are not much different from those on shore, but the consequences of even minor mishaps and any break-down in fire prevention can much more readily become

*A. S. Minton, conference paper at the Annual General Meeting of the Institution of Fire Engineers, 1961.

serious. The causes – negligence, electrical or mechanical faults, malicious ignition or whatever else – are also similar to those in buildings, but the greater isolation, lack of quick outside help, and the very nature of ship designs can aggravate a fire situation very rapidly: 'fire can spread through a ship at a fantastic rate due to the complications of alleyways, 'tween-decks and ventilating systems'.

In many ship fire cases, the shortcomings of the available firefighting equipment turned incidents into disasters. Sprinklers failed to operate due to technical or human errors, hose-reels were punctured and in a state of general decay, water supply was disconnected, extinguishers that had discharged themselves accidentally were left empty, at least in one case three extinguishers failed to discharge at the scene of a seemingly innocent little outbreak (they had not been checked for fifteen years) and the result was a total burn-out. In most cases, the confusingly varied methods of operating firefighting equipment, the lack of regular training for the crew, and fire drill deficiencies caused the loss of lives as well as ships.

Welding and repairs on board have proved themselves particularly dangerous even in port. In fact, some of the biggest write-offs ever occurred in port, during repairs, loading and refits.

When the liner *Queen Elizabeth* was being turned into a floating university in Hong Kong harbour, and when her firefighting capability was to be improved as part of the work (automatically self-closing fireproof doors were installed), a fire broke out near the stern. During the repairs, the liner's efficient sprinkler system had been disconnected. (It used to operate so well under the control of heat detectors that no outbreak during her Cunard passenger service spread beyond the area of origin.) All the 300 workmen aboard managed to escape, but the 82,998-ton queen of the sea was reduced to a mass of twisted metal.

One of the greatest refit tragedies happened in New York harbour, in February 1942. The *Normandie*, once called 'the world's most perfect ship' and 'the floating treasure-house of paintings', was trapped in America by the German U-boat menace, and the US Navy hoped to use the French luxury liner for ferrying armies – 12,000 men at a time – across the Atlantic.

As 2000 men worked on the conversion, stripping down expensive murals, boarding up the mosaic swimming pools, and installing bunks and stores, an acetylene torch sent a few sparks towards bales of life-jackets which were filled with oily kapok.

A worker tried to beat out the first flame with his bare hands. Twenty men were rolling up an Aubusson carpet, worth a fortune. They used it as a fire blanket in a vain attempt to smother the spreading flames. Others also tried to help – and accidentally, stand-by buckets of water were kicked over and wasted. Nobody thought of turning off the ventilating system: it fanned the flames towards more and more ready fuel.

Men with their hair and clothes on fire tried to escape. Others stayed to fight – in vain. More than half of the ship's 666 extinguishers were defective, French hoses were riddled with holes, the new American hose-reel couplings would not fit the French-made valves. The alarm was not sounded: it had been disconnected for repairs. Assistance was summoned by on-lookers: the first fire engine arrived twenty minutes after the outbreak. A few hours later, at 2.45 a.m., the burnt-out ship slowly capsized. More than 200 men were injured, but a miracle happened: only one man died.

An American naval officer with a great deal of wartime fire experience commented: 'I know, there were serious mistakes and equipment failures. Whatever could go wrong, did go wrong in that dreadful case, but personally, I'm convinced that the involvement of seamen played an important part: we're not used to running away from things and screaming for help. The men there tried to fight – the wrong way with the wrong equipment, I know – but tried to fight, nevertheless, until it was too late to save the ship.'

A great pity that his words were not printed in block capitals and nailed to the mast of every sailor's memory.

Only five years after the death of the *Normandie*, some 1800 miles (say 3000 km) further down the coast, in the Gulf of Mexico, it was to be a clear, warm, April day. The some 17,000 inhabitants of Texas City had started the day early. At the huge Monsanto chemical plant, and the water-front refineries, warehouses, smelters and other industrial plants overlooking Galveston Bay, the day-shifts were already in full swing, and at the Danforth elementary school nearby, nine hundred children were already in the classrooms. For ships in that beehive of a harbour, it was just a routine day.

Near the Monsanto pier, the French Line freighter *Grandcamp* was loading hundred-pound (45 kg) paper bags of ammonium nitrate fertilizer. S.S. *High Flyer*, only 600 feet (say 200 m) further up the bay, fully laden with fire-prone cargo including fertilizers and 2000 tons (2032 tonnes) of sulphur, waited for her engine turbine repairs. Her Second Mate, Ben Lapham, was on the bridge and watched the milling water-traffic, but there was nothing special to attract his attention to the *Grandcamp* – not until about 8.25 a.m., when he saw some smoke rising from that direction.

Slowly drifting smoke had already been noticed by an assistant plant manager on the Monsanto pier. It seemed rather insignificant, but he noted some commotion, too, on board the *Grandcamp*. This was at about 8.20.

In fact, it all started a few minutes earlier, down in the ship's hold, under the maze of cranes and elevators, where those paper bags were stacked high to make room for more to come. The ship was to carry a usual mixed bag – including large balls of sisal twine and thirty-foot (9 m) oil-drilling stems that weighed more than a ton (1 tonne) each.

Officers of the *Grandcamp* tried to keep an eye on all the proceedings. They knew that the 3000 tons (3050 tonnes) of fertilizer already on board was highly flammable, and one of their duties was to ensure that none of the sailors around or the

longshoremen below would smoke: a cigarette in the hold
would cost a man a week's pay.

The first puff of smoke appeared between the metal hull and
the wooden battens on which the bags rested. The gap was
no more than eight inches wide and as it was twisting and
turning, it was impossible to see or reach into it and investigate.
The four-man gang working there and the first to notice the
smoke looked for an extinguisher which could be discharged
with sufficient force to seek out every invisible nook and recess
where the fire might be nesting. All they found nearby was a
bucket.

The first bucket of water hardly disturbed the lazily twirling
finger of smoke. By the time another two buckets of water were
thrown into the gap, the smoke began to grow fat, feeding on
the ammonium nitrate. Then at last a sailor arrived with a soda-
acid extinguisher. By the time he was ready to squirt it into the
gap where the seat of the fire seemed to be, it was too late to
achieve much with a solitary extinguisher: for the second
time the firefighters were one step behind the developing
hazard.

Members of the crew above heard some shouts of warning
and quickly reeled out a hose, ready to aim it into the hatch, in
the general direction of the suspected gap. Alerted by the
sudden flare-up of activities, an officer arrived at the hatch
right behind them. As they were about to turn on the pumps,
he stopped them: even a small amount of sea-water could badly
damage much of the cargo. Once again, the fire was allowed to
have the initiative.

The men below were now affected by the growing volume of
smoke. The officer ordered everybody out. The hatch was to be
closed immediately. The idea was to smother the fire by live
steam that would do far less damage than the flooding by sea-
water. As the hatch was secured, the fire began to develop
freely – now several steps ahead of the defenders.

The *Grandcamp*'s whistle gave the high-pitched fire warning
at 8.30. The *High Flyer*'s crew, Monsanto workers, longshore-

men, passers-by, hundreds of them, began to gather all round to watch the billowing smoke and the developing spectacle.

Steam from the ship's boilers was driven into the hold where it combined forces with the smoke in increasing the pressure under the hatch covers. But the steam was no good for the purpose any more. The fire had some twelve minutes' advantage by then.

Twenty-seven firemen, more than half of Texas City's fire department, arrived. Their hoses began to fight a losing battle. And the pattern of events was still the same: the inferno had already deployed armies of flames when the fighters' reinforcements, Monsanto's own fire squad, arrived at the scene. The water could only cool red-hot metal. With the hatch closed, and the combined outward pressure of the steam and smoke sealing even the gaps around it, none of the water reached the seat of the fire below.

At nine o'clock all the crew were ordered to abandon ship. Fire and police chiefs recognized the imminence of a potential explosion, and tried – mostly in vain – to drive away the still gathering spectators.

At 9.12 the giant bomb went off. A mushroom of flames shot five thousand feet (1500 m) towards the sky. Red-hot metal shrapnel of the disintegrated ship peppered everything within a two-mile (say 3 km) radius, hitting houses, factories, rows of oil tanks. Entire sections of the ship's structure were catapulted into Texas City. Those one-ton (1 tonne) drilling stems flew off like javelins. From the air, with the rain of burning metal and other returning debris, crippled light planes and hundreds of dead birds fell on the scene of the bloodiest massacre since Hiroshima: hundreds of people were dead or badly injured along the water-front. And these were not all the casualties.

The force of the explosion hurled metal a mile (say 1·5 km) away with such force that a couple in a car were decapitated by a piece. The shock wave was recorded by a seismograph at Denver – some 900 miles (1500 km) away. A 150-ton (152 tonnes) barge was lifted out of the water by the blast: it landed 200 feet (60 m) inland, flattening rows of vehicles in a car park.

The explosion also hit the *High Flyer*: her hatches open, cargo exposed to a sprinkling of fire from the sky, the ship was forced against another freighter. Second Mate Lapham escaped with minor injuries, but many of his men were dead. He knew that below the deck where he stood, the scene for a potential second explosion was being set.

In the town there was havoc. Walls collapsing, plate glass shattered, people ducking the flying objects that included live fireballs: the sisal twine set fire to everything it touched, and rolled on and on.

The Danforth school was also hit. Many of the children were wounded. As if driven by premonition, the teachers there had always insisted on holding regular, no-nonsense, fire drills in earnest. Now preparedness was put to the test. Screaming, panicky children were ready to run. But the routine, drilled into them over the years, was now acting as second nature. The walls were cracking, but the well-rehearsed evacuation began. A large group reached an exit which was blocked. The teacher in charge there raised his hand: the usual signal to direct everybody to an alternative exit – as planned. The frightened crowd just changed direction without breaking into a stampede. School buildings began to collapse only after the evacuation had been completed.

The roads were reaching saturation point. Half the population were out in search of relatives – the other half ready to escape from the menace of a second explosion. For in the harbour, a losing battle was fought: the *High Flyer* resisted all attempts at moving her out to sea.

With the dead piled to the ceiling in warehouses, with thousands of people unable to obtain treatment for serious injuries, with mourners and desperate searchers running cease-lessly among burning and already collapsed buildings every-where, with supplies of bandages, gasmasks, welding equipment (to free the injured from under wreckage) and rescue teams arriving from other towns, and with the growing, reassuring presence of units of the Fourth Army, the burning city approached the night – but the full horror of 16 April 1947 was not quite over yet.

The fire in the hold of the *High Flyer* was already uncontrollable at six in the evening. Heroic fighters slowed down its progress enough to allow tugs to close in and try to move her. They failed, and failed again. At midnight, the explosion was imminent. Evacuation of the harbour area was never completed: a priest and rescue workers refused to leave the fatally injured to their fate. They died with them when the second explosion came and the disintegrating *High Flyer* completed the destruction of Texas City.

The town lost 570 people. More than 3500 people were seriously injured. It was said that virtually nobody escaped without some injury.

Aid poured in from everywhere and fast. Rebuilding began almost immediately. The stories of humanism and heroism have outlived the tales of horror.

Today the population of this prosperous town approaches the 40,000 mark. With the experience they or their parents had, they ought to have the most fire-conscious community, where fire-prevention is at a constant peak and there is no room left for momentary hesitation. Yet even in Texas City few people are ready voluntarily, without any prodding, when, how and how long, to fight a fire – and recognize the moment when it is time to run.

Selected Bibliography
for further reading

KIRK, Paul L.: *Fire Investigation*, John Wiley & Sons, Inc., New York, London, Sydney, Toronto, 1969

NASH, Philip: *Fire control: manual – Part 8A of Industrial Safety Handbook*, MacGraw Hill, New York, 1968

STECHER, G.: *Fire Prevention and Protection Fundamentals*, The Spectator, Philadelphia, New York, 1953

TRYON, G. H., editor: *Fire Protection Handbook*, NFPA, USA, 1954

UNDERDOWN, G. W.: *Practical Fire Precautions*, Gower Press, London, 1971

WOODWARD, C. D.: *Fire Prevention – Part 2 of Industrial Safety and Fire Prevention*, Bell's Security Handbooks, G. Bell & Sons Ltd, London, 1973

Apart from the relevant legislation and lists of FOC-approved equipment and British Standards, students of the subject would probably be interested in numerous Fire Protection Association guides and data sheets, including check-lists for fire safety in industry, small businesses and homes; management strategy for fire; how to choose, use, site and maintain extinguishers, etc.

L

Index